THIS ART

Novels

The Blinder (1966)
A Kestrel for a Knave (1968, as *Kes*, 1974)
First Signs (1972)
The Gamekeeper (1975)
The Price of Coal (1979)
Looks and Smiles (1981)
Unfinished Business (1983)
The Heart of It (1994)
Elvis Over England (1999)

Plays

Continental Size Six (Radio play, 1966)
Billy's Last Stand (1970)
Two Men from Derby (1976)
Kes (1976)
The Price of Coal (1977)
Looking at the Sun (Radio play, 1992)

Screenplays

Kes (1969)
The Gamekeeper (1978)
Looks and Smiles (1981)
Threads (1984)

Television Plays

Billy's Last Stand (1970)
Speech Day (1973)
Two Men from Derby (1976)
Born Kicking (1991)

The mainspring of my work is my political viewpoint. It fuels my energy; which is fine, as long as the characters remain believable and do not degenerate into dummies merely mouthing my own beliefs. However, I would rather risk being didactic than lapsing into blandness — or end up writing novels about writers writing novels. If that happens it will be time to hang up the biro.

My stories are all conventional in form. They have a beginning, a middle, and a sort of ending (mainly in that order), with the occasional flashback thrown in.

– Barry Hines

Barry Hines

Introduction

I first met Barry Hines about 10 years ago. I'd been sent to interview him by *The Times*. He asked me to meet him at his writing den, a small office on the campus of Hallam University, Sheffield. I remember being struck by the starkness of the room: a postcard on the wall, a desk containing a pen and a few sheets of paper, and that was about it — no books, no computer, no telephone. On the floor was a tiny kettle, able to contain just enough water to fill a single mug; I'd never seen one of these before.

Barry wasn't unfriendly but a bit gauche — a word he'd never use, of course. There is an angularness about Barry, in his movements and manner, that takes a while to get used to. He doesn't go in for social protocol, asking how you are and whether you've had a pleasant journey. This isn't for affect or to invoke any kind of power-play: he probably just forgets. After a few minutes, it doesn't matter anyway because he has an aura that coalesces kindness with straight-talking. In short, he feels good to be around.

During our conversation he often repeated the word 'wondrous'. A lot of things were wondrous: being able to work as a writer and not down the pit; Barnsley FC's current form; the standard of script-writing on *Coronation Street*; American crime novels. He sang the word, much like a kid would having just learned it.

Over the years, I kept in touch with Barry. I couldn't resist. He, among a handful of others, had made me want to be a writer in the first place. Every day he is with me, his influence, as I try to emulate the honesty and compassion he brings to his work, in my own. Also, we are brothers, working-class brothers. Although he is a generation older, I know well the people of his novels because they could be my family. My grandad worked on the railways, my mum and gran in sewing factories. The grind, the humour, the ups and the downs — it is a common history.

Barry has always been proud to write about his class but it's apparent, reading him again, that this great body of people has changed, moved on. They live in different places now, do different jobs and have different aspirations and values. This fragmentation, I believe, has been deliberate: it has suited big business. So, trade unionism is marginalised, the Labour Party has forsaken its roots and, suddenly, writers like Barry Hines start to feel like a history lesson. Where, now, are the people he wrote about? What are they doing and what are they feeling? We know too much about the under-class through unsavoury voyeuristic books written by mainly middle-class observers, and shelves groan with books chronicling the deeds of the affluent class. But what about the bloke, his wife and their kids next door to you, and me? Who is writing their lives?

When I set up Pomona I asked Barry if I could republish two of his old books — *Looks and Smiles* and *The Price of Coal*. At this point, I imagined I might possibly encounter a more anxious and vain Barry Hines: writers can be very fussy and precious about their work. He remained the same Barry I had met in that tiny room. He was flattered by my interest, trusting me with the covers and contract, happy to help in any way.

I was delighted to learn that he had a folder of unpublished work labelled, 'Early poetry, short stories.' It is from this folder that *This Artistic Life* is drawn. The stories date back many years, some to the late-1960s and early-1970s, when the success of *Kes*, the book and the film, had elevated Hines to the unexpected position of fêted writer.

Much of the work is nostalgic and mentions of 'secondary modern'; 'recs'; 'two-bob'; '11-plus'; 'silly buggers'; 'wintergreen' and kids saying, 'Soz' when they mean, 'Sorry', feel like a portal to another world.

He writes a great deal about the mining industry and two incidents in particular that have stayed with him always — the death of his grandad in a pit accident and the time he was berated by a neighbour for choosing to work (briefly) down a mine.

Tinker Lane, one of the longer pieces, feels like the first draft of an autobiography. In his trademark unadorned style, Hines tells us about the people that lived in his neighbourhood, the scrapes they got into. The writing is effortlessly simple, a sense of time and place and person brought to life.

The football stories are largely on a similar theme. *Another Jimmy Dance*, *Tottenham Hotspurs* and *The Turnstile Man* effectively feature the same protagonist — an ex-hero returning to his former club with his latest team, now older and slower, facing the ridicule of the crowd. The players — Eddie Royle, Jimmy Dance and Jackie Moon — are, what ever the colour of their shirt, brave men running their hearts out, one of a team but alone when they receive the ball. In all his work Hines innately sings the song of the underdog and in these stories he is calling on the reader to consider issues of loyalty and decency.

Hines, himself a former footballer of note, is well aware of the cruelty of team sports. In *First Reserve* we know, almost from the start, what the outcome will be for the amateur footballer who believes that preparation and comittment will earn him a place in the team. The detail in this short story is incredible. Only someone who knows — *really knows* — life in a dressing room can conjure the phrase 'puffs of dust' to describe the effect of straightening a boot lace that has been caked in mud since the last match.

There are cameos within the stories that further show off both Hines' sharp eye and the power of under-statement. In *The Turnstile Man*, we learn that the boy's father is estranged from his mother. This merits just a few lines but resonates loudly. Without revealing any more, the reader is left wondering about the family's home life, how the separation occurred, how they are working things out between them.

A father-son relationship is complex and, again, Hines states this without addressing it head-on. In *Another Jimmy Dance*, the father, exasperated by his son, scolds him and then, a few minutes later, pulls up the lad's hood when it starts to rain. Every parent will recognise this seesaw between anger and love that a child can set in motion.

The poems that intersperse the stories reveal a hitherto unseen side to Hines. Much like his writing, they are succinct, whether playful as in *Prudence Dowd* or sombre in the sketches about mining and the loss of communities that formed at pit-heads.

Once, while we were talking about books, Barry mentioned an admiration of the American writer, Bernard Malamud, in particular his novel, *The Natural*. In Barry's stories, *The End of Sammy's Career* and *Billy Peak,* he veers from his usual style and touches upon what became known as 'magic realism', of which Malamud was masterful. The short story lends itself less well to this approach but it shows Hines' willingness to embrace an idea that was very much in vogue in the late-1960s.

There is, in the very best work, always a *moment*. That point where head and heart collide. It can be a chord change in a song or a line of dialogue in a play or film that is brilliant and true. This comes, for me, in this book, in the short story, *Tottenham Hotspurs*. The father is telling his young son how to negotiate getting into a football ground. The boy wants to go through the same turnstile as his dad, but is told he can't. He asks why.

"Because that turnstile's for misters," his dad says.

In this simple sentence Hines shows us everything: the clarity of his memory; his ear for language; and his ability — perhaps a writer's greatest skill — to take us back there, making us believe whole-heartedly in the story and the storyteller. 'Back there' is a very specific sense of place, in this case to a time when we were kids and *our* dads took us to football matches and used words like 'misters'.

Many years ago another writer congratulated Hines on his 'iron integrity'. This little collection forms an eclectic hotchpotch of stories and poems, some of them tightly formed, others sketchy and whimsical, but that iron integrity is across it all and through Barry Hines, the man, too.

– Mark Hodkinson
Spring 2009

Contents

Barry's parents, Dick and Annie.

At Fitzjohn's Avenue, Hampstead,
where Barry lived in the early 1960s.

This Artistic Life

I have a room on the ninth floor of the Arts Tower. I am
writing a book in here. Every morning I clock on, sit at
my desk, write; then clock off in the evening. Very exciting, this artistic life. I don't put words on paper all the
time I am sitting here. I can't; sometimes it is too difficult
and I can't do it, and I have to sit here until I have sorted
it out. So I spend a lot of time picking my nose, cleaning
and paring my fingernails, inspecting the contents of my
desk, and looking out of the window.

This is what I can see: directly below me, a cluster of
terraced houses. Some of these houses are empty and
boarded up and it says 'EL OFF' on the doors. I'm not
sure what this means.

But there is still life down there. People stand in the
streets and talk. Dogs and cats walk about. Somebody
keeps pigeons in one of the outhouses and there are tubs
of plants growing in the backyards. It's certainly not
Belgravia but it's not a slum either. A new bathroom and
kitchen, new windows and doors, and a coat of paint,
and they'd be worth a fortune if they were in Hampstead.
Artisan's cottages they call them in the property pages.
Or perhaps they do want knocking down. I wonder if

anybody has ever asked people who live in those houses what they think about it?

Next to these houses are four tower blocks of flats. Very neat, they are. Nobody keeps pigeons in there. Or dogs or cats. Somebody might keep a budgie in a cage. There's a paved area between the flats and a circular ornamental pond. I bet the architect had heard all about the destruction of the old communities and the building of shoe boxes. Nobody was going to be able to point a finger at him. It must have looked good on paper, the pond on the new village green. I bet he thought people were going to flock down there and natter together like they did when they lived in houses. He thought wrong. The only people I see talking are people in front of the corner shops, and in the yards and streets of the old houses next door. Sometimes boys play football in the square. But they spend a lot of time fishing the ball out of the pond. Colin Buchanan* said that if he had the money, he would inaugurate a chair of Higgledy Piggledy Architecture at a university. I agree.

My room looks out over the working side of the city. I can see all the steelworks, and, surrounding this heavy industrial area, groups of council flats. One of these developments won an architectural prize. I wonder if any of the tenants were on the selection committee? Most of

* Sir Colin Buchanan (1907–2001) was a celebrated town planner who warned of the blighting effect of traffic on the environment and spoke out against the urbanisation of rural areas.

the people I write about live in places like this or in old terraced houses or on vast council estates. They work in pits and factories, and most of them have failed the 11-plus, and went to secondary modern schools.

I bet most people who live in the flats and work in the steelworks failed their 11-plus too. I bet the architect who designed the flats didn't fail his 11-plus. I bet he doesn't live in the flats either. Like most people who passed the 11-plus, he will live in a cleaner, more pleasant part of town. 'But it's the lack of space. We've got to build upwards,' explains the architect from his Victorian mansion, looking out on his back-garden the size of Wembley Stadium.

When people come up to my room, they look out of the window and say, it's not very inspiring, is it? Why isn't it? I say, although I know very well what they mean. Like a lot of people, they have romantic ideas about writing. They think you get inspiration by sitting in a cottage in the Dales and watching the sun setting over the dingle. I did that, when I first started writing. I rented a cottage on the island of Elba. I wrote at a table on the terrace and watched the sun setting over the mountains. Very romantic. But, as they say about blue movies, when you've seen one, you've seen them all. I couldn't wait to get home. After three months.

Writing is nothing to do with pretty views. It's to do with commitment. If you know what you are writing about, and what you are writing for, you could write it in a cellar. As it happens, the view from my window is very

Barry in the 1970s,
photograph taken by Fay Godwin.

inspiring. What? they say. Those horrible blocks of flats,
all those mucky factories and all that smoke pouring out?
Those ramshackle houses down there, that faceless council estate? Well, yes, I say. Most people live and work
in places like that. And I can't think of anything more
important to write about. Can you?

4

Prudence Dowd

At school, Prudence Dowd
Was not very bright.
She compensated for this
By working all day
(And most of the night.)

She had no time to spare
For appearance or looks.
Her precious life
Revolved round books.

She never dreamt
Of boys or romance,
Or had the luxurious option
Of refusing to dance.

And at college
She wasn't a sociable girl,
Which, of course, saved her the grind
Of the social whirl.

She achieved a rare state,
Where no one could reach her:
Graduated,
And became a teacher.

Photo courtesy of Martin Colman of www.kesbillycasper.co.uk

Tinker Lane

Sometimes, during dull lessons at school, I used to relieve the boredom by doodling in my rough book. I would play myself at noughts and crosses, practise my autograph for when I was going to be world famous, and sometimes, when things got really bad, write down my name and address, which transported me out of the classroom altogether.

> Barry Hines
> 62, Tinker Lane
> Hoyland Common
> Barnsley
> Yorkshire
> England
> Europe
> World
> Universe

But my universe was much smaller than that and revolved around Tinker Lane where I was born and spent my childhood in the 1940s. On a recent visit after a long absence, I was surprised how little had changed. Most of the terraced houses are still standing and so are the prefabs which were built after the war as temporary accommodation and are still going strong. The main difference is the demolition of Rockingham Colliery at the bottom of Tinker Lane, where most of the men in the village worked. There is no trace of it now. Not even a memorial. Just fields, with a motorway running through them.

The Star Inn at the top of Tinker Lane acted as a staging post for miners on their way home from work. In the 1920s when the pubs were open all day, the landlord used to open at dawn to catch the men coming off the night shift. He'd have the glasses half filled on the bar, then top them up when he heard the clatter of clogs approaching.

One morning he slept in. Thirsty miners started lobbing stones at the bedroom window to wake him up. When he eventually popped his head out to see what was happening, one of the men shouted up at him, 'Are you stopping in bed all day, or what?' It was six a.m.

The recreation ground across the road from The Star is much the same as I remember it, with a row of swings and a slide at the top of the field, and the rest of it is taken up by a football pitch. The inscription on one of the stone gate posts reads: 'King George's Playing Field.'

But nobody ever called it that. If somebody had said, 'Let's go and play in King George's Playing Field' we wouldn't have known where he meant. It sounded grand, like Locke Park in Barnsley, which had a bandstand and a café and ornamental flower beds.

My Aunty Elsie never visited Locke Park. She never

visited Barnsley, which was only five miles away with a bus every 10 minutes. 'I can't understand why anybody goes to Barnsley,' she would say. 'When you can get everything you need on Hoyland Common.' Which, in a way, I suppose was true. There was the Co-Op and the usual range of small shops. There was a cobbler who also sold shoes and there was even a draper, if you weren't too concerned about fashion. But best of all, being a gambling woman, there was a betting shop in Tinker Lane. One day, when she didn't turn up for her daily flutter, the bookie realised there must be something wrong and went round to see her. She was seriously ill with pneumonia and when she died a few days later, the bookie sent a magnificent bouquet in memory of his best customer.

During the 1940s and 1950s, when off-course betting was illegal, the local police would occasionally raid a bookie's premises and haul both bookie and his customers off to court, where they would receive a ticking off from the magistrate and a token fine.

One Derby Day, when the occasional punters had their annual flutter on the big race, police raided the derelict house in Tinker Lane where the bookie collected his bets. To raucous laughter and cheering from the neighbours, the illicit gamblers filed into the Black Maria, some of the men wearing vest and slippers, the women in pinafores and curlers. Bringing up the rear, objecting strongly, was my Aunty Elsie, minus her false teeth.

But Aunty Elsie was cosmopolitan compared to one

A scene from the film version of *Looks & Smiles*, 1981

former Tinker Lane resident I heard about recently. I had given a reading in the library in Sheffield and afterwards a woman approached me and said that she came from Tinker Lane but had moved away after her marriage. I didn't recognise her, it was such a long time ago, and I don't suppose she would have recognised me either if we'd passed in the street. But we were soon reminiscing about old times. I wonder what happened to Jack Whatsisname? You know, the usual stuff.

She told me a story about her former next door neighbour, Mrs. Watson, who had agonised for months over moving house a few doors up the lane, overlooking the rec. I worked it out. It was a distance of 200 yards at the most. Finally, she decided to flit but regretted it for the

rest of her life. She never settled up there, she said, as if
Mrs. Watson had moved to the Shetland Isles.

I imagined her, miserable and homesick, climbing the
steps of the slide in the rec, and after a longing look towards her former home, leaping to her death onto the
tarmac below. She would have had to look sharp though
or a swarm of young ruffians climbing the steps behind
her would have pushed her to safety down the chute.

A football team called Hoyland Common Health and
Sports used to play in the rec. on Saturday afternoons.
There was another local team called Hoyland Common
Athletic who played on a pitch next to the junior school.
When the posters went up in the shop windows for the
local derby game, Health and Sports v. Athletic, it looked
like a fixture in Sparta.

When we played football in the rec, the pitch was
crowded with small team games and the goalkeepers
were often distracted by dare-devils performing acrobat-
ics on the crossbars after seeing the latest Tarzan film at
the local cinema. But on Saturday afternoons, when the
Health and Sports were playing at home, the pitch transformed. The lines were marked out with sawdust. The
corner flags were hammered in and, best of all, the nets
were put up, transforming that barren field into a proper
football pitch like Oakwell, where Barnsley played. Well,
it wasn't quite as good as that but if you half closed your
eyes and used your imagination you could just about get
away with it.

During dry spells, the rec. became a dust bowl and John Parker used to wear his dad's motorbike goggles to protect his eyes. After heavy rain it turned into a swamp and one of the goalmouths became completely flooded. We used to sail boats in it and one Saturday afternoon when the away team goalkeeper was wading towards his goal before the kick off, he fell over a discarded mattress, submerged below the surface like a basking hippo. The Health and Sports supporters were ecstatic, especially as he had no spare kit and had to play the full 90 minutes soaked to the skin. I think they were disappointed he didn't catch his death of cold and have to be stretchered off, leaving his team a man short.

The Health and Sports trainer was a retired miner called Reg Crossland. We used to help him put up the nets before a match. It was always a good laugh when somebody fell off the step-ladder and Reg shouted at him to stop messing about, as if the poor lad had nearly broken his neck on purpose. Finally, when the nets were up and Reg had returned to the changing hut to deliver his pre-match pep talk, this was when the fun started. Suddenly, all the little lads rushed onto the pitch and two and three-a-side games started up in the goal mouths with the goalkeepers concentrating on which ball belonged to which game.

This wasn't as difficult as it might sound because all the balls were different. There would be an assortment of small rubber balls, an occasional worn football with broken stitches and the bladder poking through, and once, early in the season, to general amusement, a beach ball appeared, a souvenir of a week's holiday in Blackpool. It didn't last long among those hard toed boots; but weightless and travelling in slow motion, the goalkeeper wished it would last forever.

The bravest goalkeeper on the rec. was a pal of mine called Bob Johnson, who was also a daring trick cyclist. He would zigzag between the swings when they were being propelled dangerously high by teenage boys standing up on the seats and showing off to the girls. Another of his stunts was carrying his bike up the steps of the slide and freewheeling down the chute like a prototype Evel Knievel. In a rags to riches story, he would have been spotted by the owner of a travelling circus and toured the world thrilling audiences with his dare-devil tricks. In real life he left school and went to work down the pit, where there was little demand for circus skills.

When the prefabs were being built, we couldn't wait for the workmen to knock off at five o'clock so we could play on the site. Born at the beginning of the war, and never having been on holiday to the seaside, we had never seen any sand before. It was childhood heaven, an adventure playground before they were invented. When we got fed up of building giant sandcastles — they were giant because the only buckets we had were coal buckets that we'd borrowed from home — we would climb through the prefab windows and run riot in the unfinished rooms.

The builders employed a pensioner called Henry

The Hines (Annie, Barry, Richard – Barry's Brother – Dick)
on holiday, late 1950s

Gregory as a night watchman. When somebody saw him
coming, he'd shout, 'Look out! It's old Gregory!' and
we'd run away and hide until he'd gone. Farcically, Mr.
Gregory was not only old, he walked with a limp as well.
He couldn't have caught a cold never mind a gang of
mischievous seven-year-olds.

Sometimes, we'd scrape away the soft putty from the
newly glazed windows and have competitions to see who
could make the biggest ball. When I went home one
evening and proudly showed my parents my cannon ball
sized lump, they were furious and said that if I was

caught I'd be sent to Borstal, wherever that was. I couldn't understand what all the fuss was about. If we'd set fire to a prefab or buried old Gregory in a pile of sand, I might have understood their anger. But a bit of putty! It wasn't worth going on about.

It was hard to understand your parents sometimes, what they thought was important, and what wasn't. One day, I noticed that my jar of tadpoles had disappeared from the kitchen window sill. When I asked my mother where they were, she said she had poured them down the grate. Furious, I asked her why. 'Because they've been there long enough,' she replied. I stared at her. What was I supposed to make of an answer like that? Long enough for what? Did she think they'd been hanging around refusing to turn into frogs just to annoy her? But I knew there was no point in arguing. She'd have given me a clip round the ear, or even worse, sent me to bed.

One day, when we were playing in the sand outside the prefabs, we became aware of the large numbers of miners walking up Tinker Lane from the pit. Usually, there was a lot of laughter and banter when they were coming home from work, but this time they were unusually quiet and serious, and the only sound was the clatter of their clogs on the roadway. Instinctively, we knew something was wrong.

"What's happened?" I shouted.

"Doug Westerman's been killed!" one of the miners replied.

The name meant nothing to me or to any of my pals, so

after watching the silent procession for a minute or two, we resumed messing about in the sand.

Later, when I went home for tea, my mother was sitting in the armchair by the fire, sobbing into her hands. My dad, still wearing his pit clothes and unwashed, had his arm round her shoulders, trying to comfort her.

"What's the matter?" I asked.

"Your grandad's been killed," she sobbed.

I stared at her. Then the penny dropped and I realised that Doug Westerman, the dead miner, was my grandfather. I hadn't made the connection because I didn't know his name. I only knew him as grandad.

After the death of her father, I was always aware of my mother's uneasy glances at the clock when my dad was late home from work.

"Go and see if your dad's coming," she would say, and I would go outside and look down the lane towards the pit, praying that he was, so that I didn't have to go back inside and disappoint her.

When he finally arrived home, she would continue preparing dinner without any fuss. There was no ostentatious show of relief, just a quick smile and perhaps later a casual inquiry as to why he was late, all the time concealing the constant fear that her husband might be killed down the pit like her father before him.

When the prefabs were finished, my Uncle Eddie and Aunty Connie moved into one across the road from our house. I used to go there sometimes for a bath. Luckily, it wasn't one from which we'd stolen lengths of copper pipe to use as blowpipes in the jungle, so the plumbing was in good order. We didn't have a bathroom in our house, just a tin bath in front of the fire in full view of my parents and any neighbours who might have called in for a chat and a cup of tea.

It was sheer luxury at that time to have a bathroom and an indoor lavatory. Our lavatory was in the back-yard and shared with the next door neighbours. It was exciting on stormy nights though, listening to the wind and rain, and reading by flickering candlelight, the squares of newspaper stuck on the nail at the back of the door. Perhaps that's how I developed my imagination, by completing the racy stories in the *News of the World* which had been inadvertently censored by the scissors.

On Guy Fawkes' night, they held spectacular bonfires in my Aunty Connie's back garden. She made enough tins of toffee and parkin to feed the street, with enough left over for neighbours to take home. Her three sons collected the bonfire wood and sometimes she would decide that a discarded sofa left outside somebody's house was in better condition than her own, and she'd swap it.

One year, the boys couldn't wait for bonfire night to arrive, so they held a rehearsal under the table and the fire brigade had to be called out. There were sore heads and tears in the house that night after the hose pipes had been reeled in.

My Uncle Eddie, a laconic, easy-going man, was the perfect foil for his volatile wife. One Sunday dinner time

17

Richard and Barry, at Robinson's Birdbath, 1950.

she had prepared the meal for two o'clock when the pubs turned out, but on this occasion he was late home. My Aunty Connie was reluctant to start without him because the Sunday dinner was the most important meal of the week. Due to shift work, it was the only time the family sat down at the table together.

So they waited. And the meal my Aunty Connie had toiled over the whole morning was spoiling. The vegetables were drying up, the meat was going cold and skin was forming on the gravy. She kept glancing at the clock on the mantelpiece — five past, ten past, quarter past two. The children sat fearfully round the table waiting for the storm. Then, finally, in a fit of rage, she served up her husband's dinner, ran up the lane to the Star Inn and slammed down the plate in front of him in the tap room where he was still playing cards. 'Have you put any salt on it?' he asked, shuffling the pack.

Years later, when my Uncle Eddie was laid out in the bedroom, one of his sons placed a can of Special Brew in his coffin. 'He'll be ready for a drink when he gets up there,' he said. His other son considered sticking a fag behind his father's ear to go with the beer but decided that the gesture might be considered in bad taste, rather than a humorous expression of love which his father would have appreciated.

Bill Hawksworth, who lived a few doors away from us, worked at Rockingham Colliery, like my father and most of the men in the village. I worked there too for a few months after leaving grammar school at the age of sixteen. Having received no careers advice and with no idea what I wanted to do, I became an apprentice mining surveyor, which seemed like a respectable sort of job for a boy with a few O-levels.

When I went underground I took a perverse pleasure in wearing my old school blazer, as if I was trying to prove to the miners that despite my academic education I was still one of them, and hadn't deserted my roots. But Bill Hawksworth wasn't in the least bit impressed by my heroic show of class solidarity. As I crawled by him on the coal face one day, he turned round and saw me. I smiled. I had known him all my life and expected a friendly response. Instead, he shook his head. 'Couldn't you find a better job than this?' he said, disgusted that a boy with a grammar school education should end up down the pit. By his reckoning, that's what grammar schools were for, to keep you out of the pit, to gain enough qualifications to work in an office and wear a suit and tie, and draw a salary at the end of the month. And have a wife who didn't worry herself sick every time her husband was late home from work.

Bill Hawksworth's disapproval made a deep impression and shocked me into considering my future. I realised he was right, went back to school and eventually became a teacher. What puzzles me now about this episode in my life is why my parents, a sober, sensible couple, didn't make the same objections as Bill and encourage me to stay on at school. Also, what would have happened if I hadn't encountered Bill on the coal face that fateful morning? Who knows? But one thing's for sure, it's odds on I wouldn't have become a writer.

I was looking through a box of old family photographs recently when I came across one of my younger brother and me flanking the concrete bird-bath on the front lawn of Robinson's prefab across the road from our house [see page 18]. I was wearing my best trousers; thick grey flannels that made my legs itch. I stared at it, wondering why we were there. It wasn't as if the garden was full of prize blooms or had a gushing fountain to enliven the scene. There was a good crop of dandelions on the lawn but I don't suppose they would have been the attraction. Then I realised. It was the bird-bath.

We didn't own a camera when I was a child, so when a door-to-door photographer called and persuaded my mother to have our pictures taken, he would have looked round for an attractive setting. We didn't have a garden, just a communal back-yard with coal sheds and outside lavatories. It wasn't the sort of location designed to inspire the artist in him, so we finished up next to Robinson's bird-bath, which was the most decorative feature in Tinker Lane.

Most of the other photographs in the box were taken during our annual summer holidays in Blackpool, when the pit closed down for a week and most of the village enjoyed a well earned rest at the seaside. I would be playing cricket in the rec. with my pals on Friday, then continue the game on the beach the following day after

The Hoyland Common gang at Blackpool
(Barry, second left, back), late 1940s.

we'd unpacked our suitcases in the back street boarding
houses where we stayed.

A curious aside: it was perfectly acceptable for our dads
to take part in beach cricket on holiday, yet we would
have died of embarrassment if they had joined in the
games at home in the rec. It added to the fun somehow,
watching their stiff-jointed sprints when they fielded the
ball and laughing at their ludicrous excuses when they
were bowled out by their sons. They were like the pit
ponies back home which had been brought up to the
surface for the week, galloping around the paddock in
the sunlight and revelling in their temporary freedom.

There were a lot of dogs in Tinker Lane. A few were
kept in but most wandered the streets all day and were

called in at bedtime like children. Some of the dogs were always spoken of with their owner's surname attached, as if they were members of the family. For example, Barney Simpson and Toby Smith. I wonder what a stranger would have made of my complaint that I had been bitten by Prince Turner, when I took the cricket ball off him in the rec?

Most of the dogs were friendly though and you soon learned which ones you could stroke and which were best left alone. Laddie, our next door neighbour's dog, was a brute. He spent most of the day chained to his kennel in the yard. When we played cricket we quickly learned to hit the ball on the leg side because of Laddie barking savagely at mid off. If the ball went near him he would snatch it up in his jaws and carry it into his kennel. If we produced another ball, he'd be out of his kennel again before he'd finished chewing up the old one. If you're ever watching Yorkshire play cricket and you notice a batsman hitting every ball on the leg side, he probably learned his trade in our back yard keeping the ball away from Laddie.

Steve Lawton, who I sat next to at junior school, owned a whippet. It was kept in most of the time and only taken out on a lead. Being a hunting dog, it might have killed somebody's cat or caused havoc among the hens in the allotments if it had been allowed to roam free. But occasionally, if there was nobody about, Steve would risk it and let the dog out for a quick run. It was a sight to behold, pelting up and down Tinker Lane until Steve

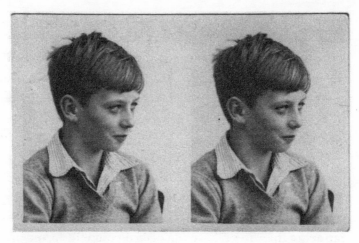
Aged nine.

called it in. One day, it snatched the joint from the roasting tin as Mrs. Lawton was taking it from the oven. Steve told me that it curled its lips right back so they wouldn't touch the red hot meat. But by the time they had wrestled the joint from his jaws, it had ripped off a huge chunk and swallowed it.

Mrs. Lawton was in a panic because her husband was due home from work and he'd be furious that his dinner had been ruined. Steve was even more worried because he was afraid his dad would be so angry — especially after that incident with Mary Johnson's pet rabbit — that he might have the dog put down. However, Mrs. Lawton managed to rescue a few slices from the savaged joint and although Mr. Lawton didn't look too happy when he surveyed his plate, all he said was:

"There's not enough meat here to feed the dog."

Four o'clock was the best time of the day. Then it was straight home from school and after a quick tea I would meet up with my pals in the rec. In the summer we played cricket or fooled about on the swings, showing off to the girls and laughing uproariously at dirty jokes that we didn't understand.

A favourite pastime was mocking old people. Mrs. Cooper, who was hideously bow-legged due to childhood rickets, was often followed by jokers walking on the outsides of their shoes in cruel imitation. Her knees were so far apart that Steve Lawton's whippet could have run between them without brushing her stockings. Her son George delivered the milk at our house and I was always afraid that he would see what we got up to and tell my parents.

We never played football in the summer. The football season ended after the cup final in early May and kicked off again in late August after we had been to Blackpool. If it was cold and raining during the summer months — which it often was — and we were shivering our way through a game of cricket, we would never dream of exchanging a football for a cricket ball even though it would have been more appropriate for the weather. There was no overlap of the seasons like there is now. You didn't play football in the cricket season or vice versa. It was as clear cut as that.

But despite the endless summer days, with bedtime deferred, the most exciting time to play out was on winter evenings under the gas lamps or roaming the streets up to mischief. It was so dark between the gas lamps that you could shout swear words without being recognised and told on to your mother.

Occasionally, if the gas lamps were out for some reason, or we were at a loose end, we went along to a wolf cub meeting in the school hall. And if we were really desperate, visited the Salvation Army in the large tin shed they called the citadel. One or two of us eventually joined the cubs but nobody joined the Salvation Army despite the attraction of learning to play a musical instrument and being in the band.

It wasn't only the hymn singing that put us off, although we had enough of that every morning at school assembly. It was the uniform as well. I enjoyed wearing my green cub jersey and took pride in the proficiency badges which my mother sewed on the sleeves. But I would rather have jumped down the shaft at Rockingham Colliery than wear that sombre Salvation Army uniform. It would have been like going to a funeral every time you put it on.

One evening, we decided to join the local library. It wasn't a sudden thirst for knowledge which drove us there, it was just another place to try out. I was wearing my roller skates and when we arrived at the door the librarian wouldn't let me in unless I took them off. This didn't make much sense to a 10 year-old, especially as there was nobody else inside. It wasn't even a proper library with tables and chairs where you could sit down and study. It was only a converted grocer's shop with a few books on the shelves, instead of bottles of Camp coffee and tinned peas.

The librarian was adamant. Choosing books on wheels seemed to offend her sense of propriety, so I skated off in high dudgeon, much to the amusement of my pals, who were thrown out a few minutes later for shouting out rude words from the dictionary.

I loved roller skating: the thrusting dash from the top of Tinker Lane to gather speed, followed by free wheeling acceleration down the long incline. Dogs could be a nuisance though, especially when you were crouched down doing the Little Man, and they were running beside you barking into your face. I was always glad Steve Lawton's whippet was never on the loose when I was travelling at that level. He'd have chased me and bitten a lump out of my arm.

My mother had the same attitude as the librarian towards my roller skates and made me take them off at the door. If I was sitting at the table when she came in from the shops, she'd lift up the cloth to make sure I wasn't still wearing them. I'd have worn them in bed if I could have got away with it.

We formed a roller skating team called Tinker Lane Tigers. We imagined we were ice hockey aces and the level stretch of roadway under one of the gas lamps became our floodlit stadium. We made team jerseys too by cutting out the tiger head trademark from Tiger sauce boxes and sticking them onto our chests.

At grammar school,
aged 11.

Unfortunately, we had no opposition, so we had to play among ourselves. We had no proper hockey sticks either, just the straight sticks that we used for fencing when we were pirates, or the three musketeers. One evening Alan Jones turned up with his grandfather's walking stick which had a curved ivory handle and this transformed him into an overnight star. Unfortunately, he ruined the handle on the tarmac and after receiving a good hiding from his mother, was never the same player again.

Shortly afterwards, during our final year at junior school, we sat the 11-plus examination. Some of us managed to pass for the grammar school but the rest of my pals failed and went to the local secondary modern. The school crest on my new blazer replaced the tiger's head on my jersey and, in a way, the break-up of Tinker Lane Tigers was the end of our childhoods.

Surprise Surprise

The placards read
> MINING DISASTER
> 30 DEAD.

Mining disasters
Are spaced through the years
Like volcanoes erupting
And snow at Whitsuntide.

Through the years
The same pit-head shots
The quiet groups,
The children strangely still.
The manager
In white official's helmet,
Stern faced
Like a headmaster late for morning prayers.

And we're shocked to read
That a few steel props
Can't hold
A billion tons of rock,

The filming of *Kes*.

That a cutting machine
Can spark a light
Causing undetected gas
To ignite.

And next time
We'll be just as shocked.
We'll pick up the papers and say
You wouldn't think this could happen today.

Another Jimmy Dance

They got off the bus and walked towards the ground. Other spectators joining the road from the side streets, made something of a crowd, and the traffic had to slow down because of people crossing, and stepping without warning off the pavements. Ian pulled his dad's sleeve and pointed ahead.

"Look, dad, you can see the floodlights. Do you think they'll put them on?"

Ronnie looked up at the sky. There were two layers of cloud; dark ones travelling fast under a wash of paler grey. When a mass of dark ones came over, it rained until the wind had blown them away.

"They will unless it clears up. It'll be dark by half-time at this rate."

He took out his handkerchief and wiped the front of his spectacles without taking them off.

"I could do with some windscreen wipers for these."

"Did you play in your glasses when you used to play football, dad?"

"No, I didn't need them when I was a lad. I didn't start to wear them until after I'd got married."

A gang of boys ran past. Dozens of them, down both pavements and in the road. They shouted the name of the home team and banged on the roofs of cars as they passed them. Most were wearing scarves, some on their wrists and belts, and as they ran the scarves streamed out like pennants. Ronnie took Ian's hand and pulled him close until they had gone.

"Bloody hooligans."

But Ian was thrilled by the episode and his face was flushed as he watched them run towards the ground.

"What are they running for, dad?"

"'Cos they're daft, that's why."

"Can I have a scarf, dad?"

They walked on and Ian had to ask again before Ronnie answered.

"We'll see how you get on."

"What do you mean?"

"Well, you might not like it. You might not want to come again."

"'Course I'll like it!"

He was indignant at his father's lack of confidence in him.

"It's not like *Match of the Day*, this, you know. This is the Fourth Division, not First."

As they approached the ground they could hear the music from the Tannoy inside. They crossed the road and Ian pointed to a group of people standing around a man in a white overall.

"What's them pamphlets they're buying, dad?"

"What pamphlets?"

"Them, look."

32

Ronnie looked, then laughed.

"They're programmes. They tell you the teams."

"Can we have one?"

Ronnie bought a programme and checked his change.

"10p? They used to be sixpence when we used to come. I mean sixpence in old money, not new."

He opened the programme to find the teams. Ian stood on his toes so that he could see too.

"There he is, look."

Ronnie pointed to a name on the visitors' team list: number 10, Dance.

"Who will you shout for dad, now that he plays for them?"

"I don't know if I'll be shouting for anybody. I can hardly call myself a Town supporter now. I haven't been for years."

He looked down the home team in the programme and shook his head.

"I don't know any of these players. They're all new 'uns to me."

He gave the programme to Ian. There was no queue at the turnstile and they went straight in. The mechanism of the gate was stiff and when Ronnie had clicked by, he had to pull the bar to help Ian through.

"It's rusty through lack of use, that's the trouble with it."

Ronnie asked Ian if he wanted to go to the toilet. He didn't, so they walked up the steps at the back of the Spion Kop. When they reached the top and Ian looked down at the ground and saw the freshly rolled pitch with the nets up, the white markings and the red corner flags, he smiled shyly at the splendour of it all.

"It's the first real football ground I've ever seen, dad."

"It's a pity they haven't got a real football team to go with it any more. Where do you want to stand?"

"Let's go nearer to the pitch."

They walked down the terracing towards the back of the goal and Ronnie chose a barrier a few steps up from the wall. There was no one else on the barrier. There was no one else within five yards of them, and there were large spaces on the Kop and the other sections of the ground.

Ronnie rested his arms on the barrier, which was mottled with rust, and Ian ran down the steps to look over the wall at the pitch. Some of the steps were cracked and crumbling at the edges and grass and ragwort were growing in their right-angles. Ian ran back up to the barrier and gave Ronnie the programme to save.

"It's a better pitch than that one in the rec, dad."

"You should have seen it when I was a lad, Ian ... "

He paused and looked round the ground, remembering it all.

"... when Jimmy Dance was playing and we won the cup, it used to be packed. We'd have had to come in an hour before the kick off to get where we are now."

Ian was looking at his watch.

"How long does it last, dad?"

"Ninety minutes. It'll finish about quarter to five."

34

"Do you think we'll get back in time for *Doctor Who*?"

Before Ronnie had time to answer, the Town ran down the tunnel onto the pitch. There was some desultory cheering and clapping which echoed round the roof of the stand and emphasized even more the sparseness of the crowd. They ran to the other end of the pitch and warmed up busily, shooting and passing and doing loosening exercises.

Then the visitors came out to the ritual abuse and moved to the end where Ronnie and Ian were standing. Ronnie found Jimmy Dance, and his smile was like the sun coming out. Dance flicked a ball up and kept it off the ground with his feet, thighs and head. Ronnie bent down and pointed him out to Ian.

"Which one?"

"Him out there, look, on the edge of the penalty area."

"Do you mean that fat 'un?"

Ronnie straightened up, his smile gone.

"That's not fat. He's always been well-built, has Jimmy."

The goalkeeper placed his cap and gloves behind one of the posts, spat on his hands and pranced along the goal line ready to receive the first practice shot. Dance volleyed the ball straight past him, high into the net. Ronnie nudged Ian with his hip and grinned.

"See that?"

"He's going bald dad, like you."

Ronnie clipped him across the back of the head with the programme.

"What do you mean, bald? He's not bald. Bald or not, I wish he was still playing for the Town. I might come a bit more often then."

The captains tossed up. The teams changed ends and the referee started the game. Ian went back down to the wall and stood near two boys of his own age, who soon lost interest and started to chase each other around an empty crash barrier.

Play was brisk and earnest. The players ran hard and moved the ball quickly. But their skill was not up to the pace they were playing at, and passes kept going to the other team. Ronnie couldn't stop watching Jimmy Dance even when the ball was nowhere near him and he was just standing waiting for it.

It was 10 years since he had been transferred, but Ronnie still saw him in the Town's colours. And although he had now played for four other clubs in a steadily declining career through the divisions, for Ronnie, he would always be a Town player. He had played for England when he was with the Town. He had scored both goals the year the Town won the Cup. Ronnie had been there to see him do it. He had gone down on Friday after work with his mates. They had got drunk and roamed Soho all night. And next day the Town had won the Cup. So they got drunk again, got locked up for the night, and when he finally arrived home he went straight to bed and stayed there for two days. It was the best time he had ever had in his life.

He had told Ian about it when they were having their

dinners and watching *Football Focus*. Ian said he had heard it before and wanted to listen to what the commentator was saying on the telly. Ronnie's wife said she had heard it a thousand times.

Dance took a pass, evaded a tackle and held the ball, waiting for someone to move into space before releasing it.

"Watch, Ian!"

But Ian had his back to the pitch and was watching a group of Town supporters singing and swaying with their scarves held horizontally above their heads. Ronnie glanced round to see what he was looking at, then called him back up to the barrier to stand with him.

"I've brought you to watch the football, not them silly buggers," he said.

"Don't you want the Town to win, dad? I do."

The Town scored first when Dance was dispossessed, leaving the Town striker a clear run at goal. He took it on and shot low past the goalkeeper as he advanced to narrow the angle. Ian jumped and clapped and cheered like the gang of lads behind him. Ronnie shook his head slowly and looked serious.

"Terrible defensive play that. There was no cover at all."

Ian started to pull at Ronnie's coat.

"Dad?"

"What?"

"I want a wee."

Ronnie looked away and swore softly.

"I can't help it."

"I asked you if you wanted to go before we came in."

"I know, but I didn't want to go then, did I?"

Ronnie led him back up the Kop and out through one of the exits. While he was waiting for Ian, a second shout went up and Ian ran out of the toilet zipping up his jeans.

"What are they shouting for dad?"

"The Town have scored again I would imagine."

"It's not fair. We've missed it."

"Well if we'd have asked them nice, they might have held the game up 'til we got back."

Ian looked up at him.

"Would they?"

He had missed the sarcasm completely and his innocence made Ronnie feel ashamed as he led him back up the steps to their place.

At half-time Ronnie bought an orange drink and a packet of crisps for Ian and a cup of tea for himself. He explained to Ian how to read the half-time scores of the other games by matching up the letters on the terrace wall with the teams in the programme. Then he showed him their programme number and told him to listen carefully for the lucky draw.

"I once came to the Town for a trial you know, Ian."

"Did you play here?"

"No, they've got a training ground out at Thorncliffe."

"What position did you play?"

38

"Half back. They don't call it that now. They call it midfield ... "

"Listen, dad!"

It was the Tannoy announcing the lucky draw. The prize was two stand tickets for the next home game. They listened for the winning number. It wasn't theirs. They were thousands out.

"Thank God we didn't win," Ronnie said, and he turned back to the team page and checked the rest of the half-time scores.

"They don't even set the teams out properly in the pro-gramme anymore. There aren't any real positions these days. Everybody seems to play anywhere now."

"Did you play well, dad?"

Ronnie finished his tea and volleyed the plastic cup down the steps.

"I wasn't on long enough to play well. They kept taking players off and bringing new ones on. There were hundreds there."

He lit a cigarette and flicked the match down after the cup.

The teams walked back onto the pitch to a few cheers and boos and the game restarted. The visitors attacked vigorously but with little wit or imagination and the Town appeared content to defend their two goal lead. They played one forward in an attacking position and left him to salvage a succession of long high clearances aimed in his general direction. It was a graceless affair.

Once, Dance slipped his marker and chipped the ball over a defender for one of his team mates to run onto and shoot. Ronnie couldn't help himself.

"Well played, Jimmy!"

Ian was surprised and embarrassed at his father shouting like that. Especially as they were standing on their own and everybody could tell who it was. The next time Dance controlled the ball it was taken off him by a Town defender who cleared it up field.

"Well played, Jimmy!" one of the boys behind Ronnie and Ian shouted. Ronnie turned on them, furious.

"What do you lot know about it? You've never seen a decent team down here."

"It's not our fault that we weren't born last century, mister."

The boys laughed and Ronnie turned back to the game, pale and trembling with anger.

"Ignorant sods. They've no idea. They never saw Jimmy when he was at his best. He scored 36 goals one season. We followed them everywhere that year. Me and the lads."

"He's too slow though now, dad. He's too old."

"Is he heck too slow. It's the others that's playing too fast, that's the trouble."

Twenty minutes into the second-half, Bamforth scored his second goal for the Town and five minutes later the visitors' trainer came out of the dugout and held up a board with number 10 on it. Dance's number. The ball went out of play and Dance walked off. He touched hands with his substitute who sprinted onto the pitch looking conspicuous in his clean white shorts and socks. Ronnie shook his head slowly.

"Bloody ridiculous. He's the only player on the park with any skill."

"I bet he's off to draw his pension!" one of the boys shouted as Dance walked up the tunnel. The others laughed.

Ronnie turned on them again.

"You'll never see a better player down here."

"You what? I've seen better players in *Dad's Army*."

They laughed again and Ronnie turned round, too miserable to argue.

"What's the point?" he said, and looked at his watch. "Do you want to go, Ian? There's not long left now."

Ian was surprised at the question.

"Do I heck! It's great. They might score again."

They didn't, but Bamforth shot against the crossbar and the boys chanted 'Bam-forth! Bam-forth!,' Ian chanting with them.

At the end of the match Ian insisted that he wanted to watch the players and officials leave the pitch before he would go. They began walking down the steps to the gate. Ian pointed to the legs of a boy in front of them.

"Look, dad, I'm going to write all the Town's players names on my jeans, like him."

Ronnie looked at the pale jeans with the names felt-tipped all over them.

"You'll have to see what your mother says about that."

"Bamforth's a good player, isn't he, dad? I wonder how many goals he's scored now?"

He stopped to look in the programme, while Ronnie, unaware of this, carried on. When he realised Ian was no longer with him he looked back, but could not see him among the crowd that converged at the gate. A gap appeared and Ronnie saw him standing there, reading the programme, oblivious of the bustle around him. Angrily, Ronnie went back and grabbed him by the arm.

"What are you trying to do Ian, get lost? I'll not bring you again if you don't behave yourself."

Ian shook the hand off and tears came to his eyes.

"What do you mean behave myself? I haven't done owt yet."

Ronnie took his hand roughly and they left the ground and crossed the road. As soon as they reached the pavement, Ian pulled his hand away and they walked down the road without speaking. It was dark now. The shop windows were lit, and the street lamps and car headlights were on. The floodlights inside the ground had disguised how dark it really was.

When they reached the bus stop, there was a queue. It started to rain again. Ronnie pulled up the hood of Ian's anorak and zipped it to the top, then he took the boy's hand and pulled him close to keep him warm. Ian did not shrug away this time but stood still and let his father hold him. There was a different kind of silence between them now.

Ian looked up.

"Dance's a good player, isn't he, dad? They were daft taking him off. Him who came on was rubbish."

Ronnie looked down at the little face in the hood.

"That Bamforth's not a bad lad either. He's definitely got the makings. I reckon they might have another Jimmy Dance there if they look after him."

"Can we come again, dad?"

"If you like. You'll not need me to bring you much longer though. You'll soon be coming with your own mates."

"I'm going to save up and buy a scarf and a bobble hat and two rosettes like them lads were wearing."

They didn't have time to say any more because the bus arrived and they had to concentrate on keeping their place as the queue pushed forward.

* Originally published in *Dandelion Clocks*, *Stories of Childhood* (Michael Joseph, 1978) and later in *The Other Half* (Akademiförlaget, 1994).

Progress at the Club

The old men opposed it,
But nobody listened.
They'd soon be as dead
As the image they clung to.

The young men ignored them,
They said they weren't with it.
Times are a-changing,
We've got to change with them.

So the old men retreated
And remembered the old days
Of sing songs
And bowling on long summer evenings.

But all that was gone now
For real entertainment,
Like Bingo and Bandits
And Strip-shows on Sundays.

So the bowling green went,
And a car park was planted
For the crews who brought in
The money at weekends.

Bell bottom jeans
Snuffing cowboy boots,
A leather jacket
Called Norton

A stance with the threat
Of Al Capone
And hair growing wild
Like a Rolling Stone.

Chewing gum
Like an American,
Under the low slant brow
Of Neolithic man.

First Reserve

George stood behind the door and watched the others getting changed. When Ted, the club secretary, came into the room the door knob hit George in the small of the back.

"Have you seen that pitch? Muddier than a watering hole."

George picked up his case and moved further into the room. Ted put his carrier bag on the floor and took out a towel and an empty bottle. He carried the bottle to the sink in the corner and turned the tap on. Nothing happened. He turned it the full length of the thread but no water came out. Ted left the tap on and re-corked the bottle. All the chromium had eroded from the tap, leaving it tarnished and pitted. The freshly exposed segment of the stem was discoloured by rust, and there was a long rusty stain in the curve of the bowl where the tap had once dripped. The bowl was dark with ancient grime and a black hair-crack pointed down to the spokes of the filter.

"They've facilities to match Wembley, here."

He put the bottle into the sink and looked at his watch.

"Roy's late, isn't he? Anybody seen him?"

The players looked round at each other, some of them

shaking their heads. One had seen him during the week, and another thought that he was working. Someone else seconded this opinion but neither was positive.

They were all changing on two benches placed against adjacent walls. There were no hooks on the walls and the clothes were piled on the benches. A length of old conveyor belt had been laid in front of each and all 10 players were crowded on to these lengths, trying to keep off the splintery bare boards.

George was standing on his own in front of the window, watching them. Three of the panes in the window had been broken and the holes were blocked with cardboard. The remaining six panes were obscured by dirt and rain. George was blocking most of the light filtering through. One of the players asked for the light to be switched on. There was no bulb in the socket so he asked George to move. George moved back behind the door.

Ted looked at his watch and asked him to nip outside and see if Roy was coming. He left the door open. The players complained about the draught. Ted pushed it to. George came in and told him that he could not see Roy. Ted studied his watch again.

"Well, it's 10-to. You'd better get changed, George."

George nodded and picked up his case. There was no room for him on the benches, so he started to change in the space near the sink. As he took his clothes off he placed the upper garments over the basin, the lower ones he allowed to remain on the floor. When he opened the

Ecclesfield Grammar School football team 1952–53.
Barry with ball.

case, his kit was revealed, meticulously folded and packed.

He took his shirt out, flapped it whole, and pulled it on. It was the best shirt in the room. It was his own. The club shirts which the other players wore were old and faded. They had short sleeves and V-necks. George's shirt had long sleeves and a round neck. There were no holes or darns in it, and the blue was still rich and deep; so different from the pale blues of the other shirts that he could have been playing for a different team. But the shirt was too tight and the clinging material revealed the full bulge of his stomach. The cuffs did not quite reach the wrists and he had to keep hooking a finger inside the collar to relieve the pressure on his neck.

His shorts were so crisp and white that they appeared luminous in the gloom of the room. But they were cut too short and they emphasised the bulkiness of his thighs.

The player on the end of the bench, next to George, tipped his boots out of a shopping bag on to the floor. They were stiff and grey with mud, and when he picked them up and bent them, clods of dry earth peeled off the soles, with the patterns of the studs punched through them. When he loosened the laces, puffs of dust came up as the dry mud scraped against the metal rings of the lace-holes.

George took out his boots and placed them together on the floor. They were almost new, with the maker's name still visible in silver on the outside. The leather was soft and highly polished, and shone black in brilliant contrast

Ecclesfield Grammar School football team, aged 12.

to the white of the laces, which had been scrubbed. Even the soles had been polished and new long studs fitted to grip the muddy pitch.

Every time George produced s fresh item from his case, the other players nudged each other, and winked, and remarked about its condition. But George just smiled and continued to get changed. He pulled his boots on and tightened the laces but the width of his foot barely allowed the laces to draw the tops of the boot together to cover the tongue, and even when they were looped in neat bows they still did not look snug to his feet.

Most of the other players were now ready. Some were standing at the window trying to look out. Some were sitting on the benches, smoking, with their jackets over their shirts. The rest spaced themselves round the room and started to throw a football to each other. It was an old ball; the stitching was strained and splitting between the panels. One of the players caught it and tested it with his thumbs.

"Hey up, Ted, has this been blown up at a garage?"

He pressed until the flesh went white under the nails but he could make no impression on the case.

"It's just like a bloody cannon ball."

It was too big for a cannon ball; more like a stone ball topping a pillar at the entrance to a public park.

George took two strips of bandage out of his case and fastened his socks up with them. He slid the knots round the backs of his legs and carefully folded the turn-overs into neat slim bands, just below the knee. He inserted a finger down the back of each sock to check that the

51

tie-ups were not too tight. He stood up and stamped his feet, wriggled his toes and looked down. The bulge of his calves and the thickness of his shin-pads made his legs massive below the knee, even bigger than his thighs.

The other players started to mill about the room, exercising, taking their jackets off and stubbing their cigarettes.

"Have we to go out, then?"

Ted stood in front of the door and shook his head.

"The ref's only just come. You'll be frozen if you go now."

"He wants to look bloody sharp then; it's going to be dark before we get kicked off."

George massaged his arms, then his thighs, with wintergreen, and the aroma permeated the room. The other players twitched their nostrils and turned round to watch him. He opened a large jar of Vaseline, scraped a dollop on to his finger and daubed it thickly across his eyebrows, forming a greasy barrier above his face. He screwed the cap back on the jar and put it back into the polythene bag in his case. In this bag was an elastic knee bandage, a clean crêpe bandage secured with a safety pin, and an assortment of smaller bandages in unopened packets. There was a tin of plasters, a selection of rubbing oils, a roll of cotton wool, a pair of nail scissors and a small brown bottle of smelling salts.

He selected the smelling salts, uncorked the bottle and sniffed at it, a nostril at a time, drawing his head back each time the fumes became too piercing. Then he replaced the bottle and combed his hair. As he was unwrapping a strip of chewing gum, the door opened and Roy rushed in, taking his jacket off as he came. The other players cheered. Roy went straight to a bench, cleared a space for himself and started to peel off his overalls.

"We'd a rush job on. I didn't think we'd get done."

George, with the chewing gum still in his hand, stood looking from Roy to Ted. Ted looked at the floor, then at the other players, and finally spoke to Roy.

"Cutting it a bit fine, aren't you? I've told George to get changed now."

"It wasn't my fault. We were just packing up when they brought this wagon in."

Already he was undressed. He opened the neck of his duffel bag and tipped his kit on to the floor.

"Urgent job, they said. There was nowt we could do about it."

The other players started to go out on to the pitch. Roy hurried his kit on, while George and Ted stood watching him. The lap of his shirt was hanging out of his shorts and his socks were round his ankles when he ran out after the rest of the team. Ted watched him go. He turned to George.

"You'd better get dressed then, George. Lock up when you come out."

He gave George the key to the dressing room and followed Roy out on to the pitch.

* Published originally in *Argosy* magazine, Volume 18, No. 11 (November, 1967).

Barry aged 12.

Sec. Mod. Boy.

Every break
Sloames 3C
Stand in a corner
Sucking sweets, seriously.
He swallows
Then sucks another,
A chain sucker.

Paper races
Round his legs,
Chased by a draught
Which bounces
And angles
From the corner walls
Like squash balls.

In class
Sloames settles down
Next to the pipes,
And slumbers through
The twilight hours
Of double Maths
And Geog.

Occasionally nudged,
He changes rooms
For Science
Or History,

Comes round at four
And sprints across the yard,
Away from misery.

Yes Sir No Sir
Pardon Sir
They are taught to parrot cry.
And let them dare
Omit our titles
And we glare
And snap Yes what boy?
Yes Sir they reply.
We nod and say
That's better boy
Then stalk away
Like overlords.

But on the bus
Or in the street
We turn away
And try to hide.
Too late!
They grin
And yell Hello Sir!
And the public turn and stare.
We hurry on
The little bastard
I'll have him Monday
For his cheek.

Bus Ride to School

When I passed the 11-plus, or scholarship as it was called in the 1950s, I went to Ecclesfield Grammar School on the outskirts of Sheffield. We travelled on school buses and the journeys there and back were easily the most interesting part of the day.

For a start, there was the ritual of getting the prized front seat upstairs when the bus arrived in the mornings. Our gang had a strategy. While the others just messed around at the bus stop, we spaced ourselves out at intervals along the pavement so that wherever the bus stopped, one of us was in position to jump on first. One time, I miscalculated the speed of the bus as I leapt for the platform and I had to grab the pole to stop myself falling off. The bus was travelling so fast that I finished up stretched out horizontal with the conductor hammering my knuckles with the ticket machine and screaming at me to get off.

The reason why it was so important to get the front seats upstairs, was to get as far away as possible from a couple of fifth-form sadists who used to terrorise the younger boys. They'd grab somebody and make him kneel down in the aisle with his arm up his back and order him to eat a tab-end or sing a song. Something like,

County Council of the West Riding of Yorkshire.

Ecclesfield Grammar School.

AEDIFICEMUS

Speech Day

Thursday, Nov. 22nd, 1951.

Distribution of Prizes and Certificates :

and Address by

Professor L. E. S. EASTHAM, M.A., M.Sc.

The Chair will be taken at 2–0 p.m., by

Alderman J. W. TRICKETT, J.P.

Express Office, Chapeltown.

58

One Man Went to Mow that lasted a long time. And we'd look petrified hoping the song would last until we reached school so they wouldn't have time to pick on anybody else. One day, they stuffed a boy up on the luggage rack, where he lay weighed down by satchels and sports kit like a miner trapped in a low seam. He was so traumatised that he stayed there after everybody else got off and was eventually discovered by a cleaner in the bus sheds in Barnsley.

The Yorkshire Traction buses, or 'Tracky' buses as we called them, would be waiting at the bottom of the drive when we came out of school. And waiting with them but slightly apart and facing the other way towards Sheffield, was a coach! A green luxury coach like the ones that went to Blackpool on The Club Trip. It seemed dead posh at the time and it carried pupils home to exotic places like Grenoside and Bradfield. I never envied them, though. It seemed like a cruel hoax, settling down on those plush seats, then arriving at the school gates instead of the seaside.

Mind you, I wouldn't have gone to the seaside on our bus if they'd paid me. Just imagine, knelt down in the aisle with 'Tiger' Jackson breaking your arm while you sang *One Man Went to Mow*, all the way to Blackpool.

Barry with actor Phil Askham on the set of *The Gamekeeper*.

Old Miners

I see old miners in the mornings
On the benches sitting back.
Pottering
In their allotments.
Or tottering
Round the quiet lanes.
Savouring daylight
Slowly,

As though draining pints of beer.
I see Old Miners in the tap room
Round the tables shuffling cards.
Or sitting back with dominoes
And old times.
Pacing bitter
Slowly.
As though draining time itself.

Then they ring the tables.
With their empty pots
And shout for more.

I saw a grimy man in overalls
Carrying daffodils,
On his way from work.
He gripped the stalks
Self-consciously
And lugged them low
Behind the knee,
Like the dead weight
Of a Christmas fowl.

But the wish-wash April Day
Flapped them in their paper cone.
And as he passed
I hoped he'd bought them
For his wife,
And not the grave.

The End of Sammy's Career

He might have got away with it in a league match, but not at Wembley. Not in front of the Royal Box.

Sammy Steel came from a footballing family and it had always been his dad's ambition to turn a full team out. He managed ten lads on the trot. When his wife died giving birth to a girl, the disappointment was too much for him, and he wasted away and died shortly after.

The children brought themselves up and perhaps this is why Sammy never learned to accept authority, even on the football field. In his last year at school, teachers preferred to cancel their fixtures rather than expose their boys to him, and when the City signed him, his headmaster strongly advised them to invest in a comprehensive insurance policy.

Sammy was tailor-made for the centre-forward position, big and fast and nasty with it, and there was something about his eyes that made opposing players feel safer when they were tackling him in twos and threes. But he was a crowd puller and his name on the programme could add 10,000 to the gate.

The City supporters loved him but at away matches extra police had to be posted round the pitches to stop people attacking him. Every time he scored he swung on the cross-bar, scratching his armpit and making chimp noises. People said that sometimes he deliberately shot wide, hoping to hit someone in the face, and, once, a spectator became so enraged that he vaulted the wall, dodged the police, and ran at Sammy, brandishing a beer bottle. Sammy waited, then kicked the ball at him as hard as he could. It smashed against the man's wrist and sent the bottle flying. Two policemen helped him off and it was reported afterwards that his wrist was broken.

Sammy was the best centre-forward in England but F.A. officials said he would be a bad ambassador for English football, and always used this as an excuse to pass him over. The newspapers were more interested in results, especially with the World Cup coming on, and after a fierce campaign on Sammy's behalf, the F.A. were forced by public demand to watch him. They attended *en bloc*. Sammy scored four goals in 12 minutes and was turning away after heading his fifth when the referee blew for offside. Sammy disagreed and grabbed him by the lapels. The referee warned him but it made no difference, so he took out his little notebook and asked Sammy for his name. Sammy whipped out a similar book from somewhere down his shorts and asked the referee for his. The referee sent him off.

It was Sammy's goalscoring that took the City to Wembley that year. The week before the final, he appeared on *Sportsview* and caused an uproar when he told the interviewer that he would score a hat trick, and even named the minutes when the goals would come.

He scored in the eighth and 51st minutes, exactly as he had predicted. Then it happened, four minutes before his next goal was due. The ball ran out of play and as Sammy ran to retrieve it, a streaming toilet roll flew out of the crowd and hit him smack on the nose. A gang of spectators cheered and spun their rattles. Sammy wiped his nose with the back of his hand, picked up the toilet roll and walked across to them, the loose end trailing like a kite tail. He reached the wall and stopped. The crowd quietened. Sammy turned and slowly pulled his shorts down. When they were round his ankles he tore off a length of paper and used it. Right in front of the Royal Box. Before Royal eyes. One hundred thousand people drew breath sharply. Sammy scrunched the paper into a ball and lobbed it into the crowd. Wembley exploded. He hadn't even pulled his shorts back up when two big men in dark overcoats strode on and gripped him at either side. They almost dragged him round the pitch to the tunnel. It was the last time Sammy ever left a football pitch. It was the end of his career. They wouldn't give him a medal, even though his two goals won the cup for the City.

A Dead Hyacinth

I tried to straighten
A dead hyacinth,
And managed to prop it
Between the leaves.

But even then
It still looked dead,
So I yanked it out,
Because the dead
Can't be disguised,
Whatever pose they
Care to adopt.

Neck and neck, the Tough and his rival break the tape together. Who has won? Only the judges can tell!

THE EARLY DAYS OF THE TOUGH OF THE TRACK

IT was Friday night and Alf Tupper, the lone wolf athlete, stood in a crowd on Greystone station. A muffler was knotted round his neck and his clothes were threadbare. He earned twenty-five shillings a week as an apprentice to Ike Smith, a welder.

The loud-speakers were switched on.

"The next train to arrive at Number One platform will be the ten-thirty-five express to London," said the announcer. "The sleeping cars will be found in front of the train."

Alf stayed where he was, but he saw a group of young men, in dark red blazers, move towards the top end of the platform. They were members of the Greystone Hall Athletics Centre, set up for the improvement of British athletics, and their destination like Alf's was the White City Stadium in London.

The Amateur Athletic Association Championships were being held next day, and Alf was running in the mile.

The train steamed in. There was a rush towards the carriages. As usual at the week-end, a lot of people were travelling and the train already looked full.

"I ain't standing all night," muttered Alf. "I want a spot of shut-eye."

Alf drifted along the platform. The double doors of the guard's van were open, and two porters were loading luggage.

Alf was through the guard's door and into the van in less time than it took to wink. He stood clear of the window till the double doors at the rear were banged. Then he nipped down the van, slipped behind a pile of luggage, and, with a mailbag for a pillow, stretched himself out on the floor.

The train soon started, and he heard the guard bang the door. As all the luggage was for London and required no sorting out, he did not come down the van. Alf settled down for a nice sleep.

Alf was awakened by the creak of doors and an angry voice.

"Come on out of it!" snarled a parcels foreman, glaring down at Alf.

"You ain't tipping me out," snapped Alf. "I've a ticket."

"This is London, and let's see your ticket," said the railwayman.

Alf grinned and produced the ticket. It was examined and found correct.

"What have you got in that parcel?" asked a railway policeman, looming in the background.

"You're welcome to have a look, chum," said Alf. "They're my running togs."

"Hop it," said the policeman. It was just after six o'clock on a grey and chilly morning as Alf walked down the platform.

With five shillings and his return ticket, Alf had the day in front of him. He bought a newspaper and went out to find a cafe. In a back street place used mainly by railway workers, he was served with a cup of strong tea and a plate of baked beans on toast.

Alf turned to the sports page of his paper. There was a good half-column about the A.A.A. sports. The paragraph that interested him was—

"Given good running conditions, four minutes ten seconds should be at least equalled in the mile. Great interest will be taken in the first appearance in London of Rob Lackman, the Greystone discovery.

"Commander Harold Churcher, the Warden and former Olympics relay runner, has high hopes of Lackman, who, while of British birth and parentage, has only recently returned to this country from America, where he has had the advantages of the intensive coaching methods at Penhurst University, Illinois.

"He will have a strong challenger in the improving Arthur Mills, of Bristol, and Reg Keller, of Newcastle, has yet to show his best form in an A.A.A. event.

"The unpredictable Alf Tupper, who has put up several startling performances this season, is running and, while not having a real chance, will finish strongly. His style is against him, powerfully as he runs."

Alf sniffed scornfully.

"Lackman!" he muttered. "I'll show him the way to go home."

The White City crowd picked out Lackman the moment he came out on to the track. He was a powerfully-built fellow.

"Get to your marks!" shouted the starter.

"Get set!"

The gun! Alf was away with the bang, but Lackman was in front of him. The big fellow had started like a greyhound and was on his way.

To the onlookers Lackman appeared to be striding slowly, but Alf and the other men behind him realised how fast he was covering the ground. Though he was perfectly balanced, his stride was of tremendous length.

Alf's style was far from graceful. His shoulders were hunched so that he seemed to be butting his way along, and his arm movements seemed jerky.

The pace was fast, but Alf felt comfortable. What satisfied him was that Lackman was not widening the gap.

It was in the third lap that Alf felt his left shoe sliding up and down his heel. It was not loose enough to slow him down, but he was aware of it all the time.

The third lap was run at a cracking pace, and Alf wondered if he would have anything left to challenge Lackman at the end.

The runners came round, and the bell clanged for the last lap. Almost at once Alf passed Mills. He went by him in a couple of strides and hung on to Lackman.

Alf knew he had a bit left, and he watched Lackman for signs of a spurt.

When it did come, it took Alf by surprise. He suddenly realised that the leader was speeding up. The gap was quickly four yards instead of three. The spectators, too, saw that Lackman was making his final bid.

Alf drove himself forward in his spurt, and his left shoe came off. Thousands of spectators did not see it, for he scarcely faltered. His bare foot thrust at the hard track, and, wearing only one shoe, he chased Lackman in.

The tape was across the track, and Lackman was racing for it. He was going flat out, and the tremendous dash of the perfect athlete brought roar after roar from the crowd.

Alf was coming up, throwing everything he had into his final spurt as he raced for the tape.

Head back, Lackman drove for the tape. Alf felt the end whip against his cheek. The crowd was in a tumult. Nobody knew who had won.

The spectators did not know. The judges were still huddled together.

Lackman was pumped on, and so was Alf. They were lying near each other, gasping for breath.

The loudspeakers crackled and the crowd hushed for the announcement.

"In a close finish, Rob Lackman was first in four minutes nine and four-fifths seconds," rasped the voice. "Second Alf Tupper, third Reg Keller."

INTERNATIONAL INVITATION.

ALF had his jacket off on the Tuesday morning. Metal clanked as he unloaded a van that had brought in metal for welding.

The postman plodded up the alley and handed Ike two or

The Rover, June 28, 1958.

66

Fiction in the Classroom

At grammar school, the only subjects I was interested in were Physical Education and Games. English, double chore, because it was divided into two subjects, English Language and English Literature. This meant we had to sit two examinations after five years, instead of one.

English Language was a sort of word spotting game. We seemed to spend a lot of time dissecting sentences, extracting the individual words, labelling them, then placing them into little boxes, which were connected to other little boxes with words inside. This was called 'clause analysis'. It seemed to be a pretty important thing to do at the time. I couldn't do it. I still don't know what it was all about.

English Literature was reading books about people who had been dead for hundreds of years. They had to be dead for that long or it wasn't literature. It was all long frocks and chandeliers. The books came out of the cupboards looking like a pile of house bricks and when you opened them, there were 5,000 words on every page. The teachers were always talking about the authors' style. I wasn't too interested in that. I wasn't interested in the problems of keeping the silver clean, either. Or the difficulties in getting your daughter married off to a rich young buck. It was all too posh for me. I resented it. I felt I was being imposed upon by middle-class teachers in a middle-class institution glorifying upper-class values.

I wanted to read about a world I could identify with, where people had to work for a living. Nobody seemed to work in literature. I wanted to read about Teddy Boys and courting and sport and adventure, and the only place I found it was in comics. In the sixth-form, when most of the students were reading books, I was still taking *The Rover*. The sports stories were my favourites: Nick Smith the scheming inside forward, and his mate Arnold Tabbs the ex-ironpuddler; Alf Tupper, the Tough of the Track. Alf was the first four minute miler — you can't count Wilson in *The Wizard* because he was super-human. Alf carried his kit in a brown paper parcel. He was a welder by trade and he ate a lot of fish and chips. I understood all that. Alf was my hero.

I never read the school stories, which, of course, meant public school stories. Nobody went to state schools. There were no girls alive either. The whole child population of this country was composed of young gents raiding tuck shops and climbing out of dormitory windows on midnight japes. I thought they were cissies. They were nothing to do with me. They might as well have lived on Mars as far as I was concerned. I met my first public schoolboy when I was eighteen. I was right. We did live in different worlds.

I was still reading comics when I went to Loughborough Training College. I went there to study

Physical Education. My real ambition was to be a professional footballer but if I didn't make the grade the next best thing seemed to be a Physical Education teacher. It was at Loughborough that I became interested in reading books. And it was purely by chance. I was in lodgings with a boy who was doing subsidiary English. My second subject was History. He had bought some books for his course and one Sunday afternoon when it was raining and I was bored, I asked him if I could borrow one. He looked doubtful; he hadn't got any picture books. So he found me the thinnest book on his shelves. It was George Orwell's *Animal Farm*, 120 pages, nice large print. I read it at a sitting. It was the first book I had read of my own volition. I can't remember now what I got out of that book that was so special. But I had enjoyed it. I realised that reading books could be enjoyable.

Then I read *The Road to Wigan Pier*. I was on my way.

View from a Bus

The man on the pavement side
Sat up in anticipation.
Then the bus stopped
And they all flopped back in frustration,
Riddling the driver's neck
With looks.

She was a classy bird,
Even from the back
They could all tell that,
By her sunburnt legs
And the confident swing
Of her well-oiled hips.

They pressed an eye to the glass,
Then relaxed
As she reached a car showroom
And stopped
To stare at the grinning ranks
Of smooth seducers.

Teaching P.E. in Barnsley, early 1960s.

When the bus passed her
They swivelled their heads
Like owls.
But her face remained hidden
Behind a golden wing.
And all the time
She looked in
Looked in.

Billy Peak

Some said that Billy Peak was the greatest tennis player of all time. Some said he was mad. He never disputed either statement and both were probably true.

Nobody knew where he came from. Some said he lived in Yorkshire, on the moors, and that he practised behind high walls against an unbeatable machine. They said he once captured a snooper and tennis-balled him to death with it. Others said he was released annually from a lunatic asylum to play at Wimbledon. But nobody ever found out.

He played three times at Wimbledon. The first time he won the men's singles. The second time he was suspended. And the third time he was killed in the final.

He caused a sensation on his first appearance. He wore shorts that many thought obscene, and black pumps and no socks. After he had won the final he just got dressed and left. When a newspaper man tried to follow him, Billy Peak grabbed him round the throat and threatened to push him under a bus. The newspaper man straightened his tie and wrote a story about it.

The crowd hated him because he was ugly and unbeatable. They booed him when he won but the court was always packed when he played. Once, during his first appearance, two men picketed the gates with placards which read 'PEAK SHOULD NOT PLAY: KEEP AWAY'. But when the gates were opened one of them was seriously injured in the rush, and the other had to use his placard to defend himself. This excitement had been caused the previous day when Billy should have played Von Vim. He came on court with a racket cover which, instead of 'DUNLOP', read: 'GERMAN GO HOME'. Von Vim withdrew in protest and Billy passed through to the next round.

The other players hated him. They said he never spoke to them in the locker room. But he was not dumb, because he cursed all the time on court, making people go red and the umpire warn him. The players said he should be banned. They said he aimed the ball at them and that when he had broken the nose of Ginsberg, the American, it had been deliberate. They also said he wet the ball with sweat from his brow. And that when he was serving he wouldn't hold the new balls up to show them.

He wouldn't bow to the Royal Box, either. The first time he walked straight past, people thought he had forgotten and laughed. The second time, a man at the back stood up and shouted: 'Communist'. A fight started and three men were arrested for disturbing the peace. Once, he smashed a ball so hard that it bounced up among the Royalty. Many people said he had done it on purpose, and security officials were called in to check the balls, to make sure there were no bombs under the fur.

When he won the final he didn't bother receiving the

cup. He walked off while they were still lining the ball boys up and unfurling the carpet. So, Her Royal Highness presented the cup to the loser instead and told him that he had played very well under the circumstances and would he please pass it on. The officials said that he would be banned next year. But the newspapers said they couldn't ban the first British champion since 1936 and people wrote letters to support them.

The following year, he appeared on court carrying a racket and a flask. When they stopped for refreshment he wouldn't drink from the official container under the umpire, but swigged from the flask instead. Some said it was a secret herb brew, distilled on the moors. Others said it was booze and the people on the front row swore they could smell his breath a mile away. The officials investigated; it was cold tea.

He was leading 6–0, 6–0, 4–0, when he made his first bad shot. He walked to the centre and smashed the racket strings down onto the iron post. Then he snapped the handle across his knee and threw the hanging mess into the crowd. It landed in a woman's lap. People screamed and rushed at her, grabbing for pieces of the broken racket. When order was restored, the woman had been stripped to the waist. She had to be taken to hospital and treated for shock. He won the match with a racket selected from his opponent's stock.

In the next round, using the same racket, Billy served an ace to open the game. The line judge called out. Billy walked up to him, turned round, and dropped his shorts.

74

Women screamed. The umpire stood up in his high chair and took a step forward. Billy was suspended.

When he returned for the third time, the officials had to plead with the other players to make them stay. In the first round the umpire warned him about singing on court. A clergyman rose and left because he wouldn't stop singing Jesus wants me for a sunbeam. In the next round he was seen to blow his nose on the ball when about to serve. He threw it up with the snot facing his opponent and when it hit the ground it skidded ankle high and hit the leg of a line judge. He looked down then wiped his trousers with a handkerchief. Billy's opponent protested and he had to serve again. In the third round he put so much back spin on one shot that it bounced straight back over the net to him. The crowd was in uproar and a ball boy was sent running for a rule book. In the semi-final he let his opponent win one game by refusing to play the ball. The umpire warned him but he just curled up on the ground and rocked from side to side. Some said that he was resting, others that he practised Yogi. But when he stood up and served, he struck the ball so hard that many people swore they saw the grass flare where it hit the ground. On inspection the ball was found to be scorched. One of the ball boys pocketed it and later sold it to an American for £100.

Billy Peak was killed in the final. He was leading 6–0, 6–0, 5–0, and was serving for the match when a man stood up and shot him in the back. Billy staggered. The crowd jumped to their feet. Billy steadied himself, tossed

In Germany, 1990.

the ball up, then dropped flat on his face. His opponent
threw his racket away and leapt the net. Some danced
with joy and cried into each others arms. Others chased
the assassin onto the court and battered him to death
with Billy's racket. Someone set the net on fire and
70 people were killed in the stampede to get out.
Wimbledon was closed down after that. Some blamed
the assassin but others blamed Billy Peak himself. They
said he should never have been allowed to play in black
pumps in the first place.

How to Make Poets Rich

I like hardback books
Of poetry.
They're slim and neat
With good stiff pages
And clean print.

Unlike the novel
You can read them in the shop.
And that's the trouble.
Too many browsers
And not enough buyers.

They should be sealed
With cellophane. Like sex books.
That way, you'd have to buy
To open them.
Poets might make some money then.

Perhaps I'd buy one too.

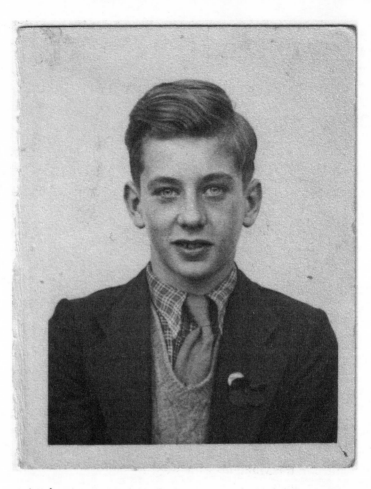

Aged 13.

Your Death of Cold

I started watching Barnsley when I was in junior school at Hoyland Common in the late-1940s. After the match, I would stand with my pals outside the Players' Entrance waiting for them to come out so we could collect their autographs. And what a long, cold and sometimes drenching wait it was before they emerged, flushed from the bath with their hair still damp. Most of the players were good-natured and willing to accommodate the throng of little boys pushing autograph books into their faces, but a few refused, brushing us aside and hurrying from the ground. I couldn't understand why. Being famous and surrounded by autograph hunters was every little boy's dream.

I had some famous names in my book, including Stanley Matthews, Danny Blanchflower and Tommy Taylor, who broke our hearts years later when he was killed in the Munich air disaster.

Recently, I read in the paper that Leon Leuty, another famous player of that era, had died. He was a stylish centre half who played for Notts County and won a couple of England caps. He'd have been an England regular, if it hadn't been for the consistency of the Wolves and England captain, Billy Wright.

Reading about his death brought back memories of an incident outside the ground. It was throwing it down and I was sodden after standing on the uncovered Kop all afternoon, followed by a long wait for the players to appear. Rather than sign autographs standing in the rain, the Notts County players took pity on us and invited us onto the team coach which was sheer luxury, with a carpet down the aisle and tables with individual lamps. It was a bit different to the Yorkshire Traction bus, the 'Jump circular' we were going home on.

I had a cigarette card of Leon Leuty in my scrapbook. If you featured on a cigarette card, it meant you were famous. I stood there thrilled, watching him sign my book. When he handed it back he smiled, and said:

"Go home now or you'll catch your death of cold."

I just stood there, astonished that an international footballer was concerned about my health. When you're a child, you never think that your heroes care about ordinary things like catching a cold. They're gods who exist solely on the football pitch, then disappear somewhere until the next match. It spoiled it somehow if you imagined them sitting by the fire with a pot of tea, like your dad.

But I'll never forget Leon Leuty's kindness on that wet afternoon outside Oakwell and I was sorry to read he'd died.

L. LEUTY

Two Old Ladies

The light
Seeped through the stained glass door
Like sulphur fumes.
It opened wide
And two old ladies stepped outside,
Sniffing the night
Suspiciously,
Like rabbits
Ill at ease before the hutch.

The street was dark
And full of bogey holes
Behind the privet of house fronts.
So still
Until a cat leapt from the shrubbery
And made the two old ladies hug each other,
Whimpering
And whispering.

Good night Miss Tibbs.
Good night my dear.
Same time next week?
Yes, all being well.
Sleep tight my dear.
Don't worry dear.
I will.

The Big Match

I've never played a game of football in my life. I've always played in *matches*. I was brought up in an area dominated by professional football clubs — Barnsley, Sheffield, Rotherham, Doncaster, Huddersfield, Leeds. There were no prominent amateur clubs to watch, so my attitudes were formed on the terraces at Oakwell, Hillsborough and Bramall Lane.

There were hundreds of local football teams around but these were never amateurs either. Not in spirit anyway. They were composed of lads who were aspiring to be professionals or men who hadn't made it. The game was never the thing. Only the winning. The only good matches were the ones you won. It was as simple as that.

At grammar school they thought differently. They even wasted part of the field on a pitch which had funny markings and two flag poles stuck at each end. I still think there is something unsatisfactory about rugby posts. There is no real end to them for a start. If you kick the ball five miles high and the referee judges that it would have gone between the posts, then it's a goal.

But even then it is not a real goal, is it? Real goals are under the cross-bar. And they have nets. I can never get worked up when I see a rugby player taking a penalty

England Grammar Schools (Barry second right, back row).

kick, no matter how far the distance or how narrow the angle. After all, he only has to kick the ball over the bar and there's nobody trying to stop him.

Footballers do this all the time and get jeered and cursed for it, even though they are running with the ball, or being tackled, or being blocked by a wall of players standing five yards away instead of ten. No, if there was a goalkeeper up there between the posts, suspended by balloons, or with a helicopter strapped to his back, I might be able to take it more seriously.

I even find the markings on a football pitch satisfying; their symmetry, the matching halves of boxes and curves.

It is as pleasing to the eye as the doubles in dominoes. I'm surprised no artist has painted a football pitch yet, just the white lines on a green background. Hanging in a gallery, nothing else would get a look-in. There would be a crowd round it all day long waiting for the teams to come out.

At grammar school they also tried to convince me that football was not really important, that games lessons were merely half-time breaks between the academic rigours of the week. But what they did not understand was that I was not an academic boy. All I wanted was to be a professional footballer. Football and running were the only things I was any good at.

At school I lived from games lessons to Saturday morning matches, year in, year out. The agonies I've sat through staring out of the window hoping that the fog would clear or the rain would stop before the games lesson. The weeks that have been ruined when the teacher said the weather was too inclement and we would have to go into a classroom and have a quiz. There's a grammar school teacher's word for you, inclement. When we couldn't play at home it was because it was pissing it down.

We didn't play in leagues either. There were no cups and we couldn't play for the district team. That was only for the local secondary modern school lads. This used to infuriate and frustrate me, the way we were supposed to regard ourselves as above this kind of competition. Why did they want to make us feel superior? Just because I sat down one morning when I was 10 years old and got a few more sums right than my mates seemed no reason for trying to make me into a snob. Yet, this is what they tried to do. Not overtly, but the very existence of the school meant they had no choice.

Like the public school, the grammar school exists to perpetuate the class divisions within our society. They are middle-class institutions which try to seduce the working-class student into their ranks.

They failed with me. When my mates left secondary modern school at 15, I wanted to leave with them. I applied to the local pit for a job as an apprentice mining surveyor. I didn't want to be a surveyor but it seemed a respectable sort of job; I would be on the staff. Even I wasn't immune from all the indoctrination that was taking place around me.

The chief surveyor said: 'You need O levels for this job. Go back to school and get some'. So I went back and got some. And when I knew the rainfall on the Pampas and Gladstone's foreign policy, they employed me as an apprentice mining surveyor. I stuck it for six months.

I went back to school and decided to become a PE teacher. I thought that if I didn't make it as a professional footballer, then teaching physical education would be the next best thing. Like football, I didn't regard it as work. I didn't want to be a teacher. To my mind they were on a par with the police, agents of repression. No, it just seemed like a very pleasant way of perpetuating my adolescence.

I think this is one of the reasons why I never made it though. I took out an insurance policy. I wanted something to fall back on. I was a decent player but I would have been a lot better if the only alternative had been working all three shifts down the pit, like my dad.

It was while I was in the sixth-form that something very significant happened to me. I was chosen to attend the Schools Week at Cambridge. About 100 of the supposedly best grammar school and public school footballers were picked to take part in a series of trial matches, the aim being to find the best team to play Scotland under-18s.

I went down on the train from Sheffield, full of myself. I was 17, fit, fast, strong and reasonably skilful. I was playing for Yorkshire Grammar Schools and several League clubs were interested in me. A Manchester United scout had been to our house and this was at the time of the great team, just before the Munich disaster.

I went down in my suit — I was a semi-Ted at the time — drape jacket, tight trousers, crew cut, D.A. When I saw those public schoolboys, I couldn't believe it. They didn't seem to have heard of fashion. They were all dressed in flannels and sports jackets with sloping haircuts. They would have looked well in the officers' mess in a British war film. Nigel Patrick* would have been their commanding officer.

* An English actor (1913–81 and stage director, who, following a leading British male in films such as *The Sound Barrier*, *The League of Gentlemen* and *Sapphire*.

"Northern Herbert."

But it was when we talked together that I really felt the difference. They were so articulate and so assured. They had a collective air of massive superiority that staggered me. And suddenly I didn't want to talk. I was embarrassed by my clothes. I was a Northern Herbert in yellow socks and bumpers. They tolerated me. After all, they were too well bred to be rude, but all the time I felt I was being politely patronised. Disraeli was wrong when he talked about two nations. It is more like two worlds.

The only place I could match them was on the football pitch. I didn't have to say very much there. Some of them were good players, but even the best lacked the urgency and determination of the working-class grammar school boys. But then, what had they to be urgent about? Football was not important in their lives. For them it really was a game.

They had more studied destinations. They were from wealthy influential families. They were destined for Oxford and Cambridge and then positions which would in turn ensure and perpetuate the wealth and influence of their own class. What was the tawdry glamour of football, compared to the stealthy power and affluence they were going to achieve?

I began to realise that playing for Barnsley for £20 a week wasn't the real big-time, after all. It was a tin-pot, a mere diversion, compared to that other world I was now getting a sniff at for the first time.

I made the England team. I watched every match I did not play in to assess all the other wing-halves on the course. There was only one danger for my position, a boy from a southern independent grammar school. But he got injured. I was glad. He was no better than me but he might have been picked because he looked more respectable and would certainly have known how to speak to waiters better in the hotel in Glasgow.

We played Scotland at Celtic Park. I can't remember much about the match except the score: we lost 0–3. It didn't seem all that important though. What had been much more valuable was the political experience, seeing the class system at work close-up. For the first time I had been able to place football into some kind of social perspective.

For the real winners, of course, are those who play it as a game. Me? I'm still trying to get a team together, and keeping in training for the big match.

* First Published in *The Times Educational Supplement*, 2 May 1975 and in *Sport* (Oxford University Press, 1991).

School sports day

You Can't Beat a Cig Packet

I could have clocked a wonder time.
If I had wanted,
I could have beaten Batman
If I had raised my flaps
And let the gale strain at my tweedy wings.

A cig packet tumbled past
Clip clopping as it bounced along.
I gave it a start
Then chased
And raced behind it for a hundred yards.

But then I tired
And tried to stamp it with my foot.
This broke my stride
It cart-wheeled on.
I stopped
And watched it out of sight.

Well!
You can't beat a cig packet
Helped by a gale
Along a straight
And empty road.

Tottenham Hotspurs

"Take our Neil with you, Frankie."

Neil was playing on the floor with his toy train set. Coupled to the train were two coaches and an open wagon carrying two soldiers, one standing, the other kneeling, both firing rifles. The rails described one tight circle in the centre of the ring. Every time Neil released the train he placed matches across the rails to derail it when it came back to him. The soldiers fell out and lay on their sides, still firing. Sometimes the wheels of the train ignited a match head so there was flame and smoke to heighten the disaster.

"That's what they do on cowboys."

"Well you can just stop it. You're ruining that rug with your matches."

His mother bent down and started to collect the matches but she soon stood up again, puffing and holding her stomach.

"It makes me puff when I bend over like that."

She massaged her stomach and watched Frank tie the knot in his muffler.

"Are you taking him, then?"

Frank spread the knot and tucked the fringe down his overcoat.

"Our Neil's not bothered about coming, are you, love?"

"Where you going, dad?"

"Down to watch the Town."

"They're no good."

"Who says they're not?"

"Everybody at school supports Manchester United and Liverpool, and Hotspurs."

"The Town used to be as good as any of them."

"Dad?"

"What?"

"Why do they call 'em Hotspurs?"

"They don't call 'em Hotspurs, it's Hotspur, Tottenham Hotspur, that's their name."

Neil went back to his train, chanting quietly to himself 'Hot-spurs, Hot-spurs,' while he prepared the coaches and the soldiers for a fresh disaster. Frank began to check his pockets, money, handkerchief. Shirley handed him his cigarettes and matches from the mantelpiece.

"Go on, take him, he'll enjoy it."

"I might be able to have a lie down for an hour, then."

"I'll take him another time. He'll be frozen this afternoon."

"He'll not if he's wrapped up properly."

"It's raining, you know."

"You can go under cover, can't you?"

"There is no cover on the Kop."

"Go somewhere else then. They open other parts of the ground, don't they?"

"I know, but it's not the same anywhere else. All the lads get on the Kop. That's where we always used to go."

He smiled, and for a moment his eyes were as abstract as his son's, planning sabotage by the fire.

"He'll be fed up to the teeth after five minutes. There's nothing at the Town now; no players, no excitement. There'll be nothing going off worth seeing."

"How do you know, you haven't been for years."

"I don't have to go, I know. It's the same everywhere in the Third and Fourth Division."

"Well, if it's that bad, what are you going for?"

"I don't know. It'll be a change."

"You've picked a grand afternoon for it."

They looked upwards to see over the net curtain covering the bottom half of the window. Above the houses across the street, the sky was an even grey wash. The slates of the houses had been darkened and polished by the rain, and the colour of the sky reflected in them.

"Anyway, Eddie Royle's playing."

"Who's Eddie Royle?"

"He used to play for the Town, years back."

"I thought you said he was playing today."

"He is, he's playing for the others."

"Oh, I see."

"He's one of the all-time greats, is Eddie. He was mar-vellous ten years back with the Town."

"Our Neil'd like to see Eddie Royle, wouldn't you, love?"

"Our Neil's never heard of him."

94

"I have. I have. I've seen him on the bubblegum cards. He played for England."

Frankie smiled, and nodded at him.

"Have you got one with him on?"

"No, but I've seen him at school. Some kids have got him."

"I bet the Town wish they'd got him. Like he was ten years ago. He'd have them back in the first division all on his own."

Neil set the train running, then stood up.

"Can I come, dad?"

The train completed the circuit and for the first time continued intact. Frank looked at the television. He watched the horses leaving the paddock, then he looked at the clock on the mantelpiece.

"Look sharp then, else we'll miss the kick off."

"Hurray!"

Neil ran into the kitchen and started to pull his Wellingtons on. His mother made him take them off again and put on an extra pair of socks. Frank sat astride the arm of the settee and watched the horses going up to the start. The jockeys showed them the first fence. Some of the horses backed away and threw their heads. Some just looked quietly over the other side. The jockeys turned them round and took them to the tapes. Shirley tucked Neil's scarf in while he fastened the pegs of his duffel. He left the top peg unfastened. Shirley fastened it and pulled up the hood.

"Oh, mam, I don't want that up."

He tried to pull it down but his mother stayed his hand.

"Leave it on, it's raining."

"Oh, mam."

"He's ready, Frank."

One of the horses wouldn't have it at the start. It kept coming into line, then backing out and wheeling round. The other jockeys were shouting, but what they were shouting was inaudible.

"He's ready, Frank."

"I wish they'd got a mike close to that lot. I should love to hear their language."

A man in a trilby tried to lead the horse in but it backed away and dragged the man with it. He lost his hat, and let go of the horse to retrieve it.

"Come on, dad."

"There's plenty of time, Neil. There's no crush at the Town now. You can walk in at five to three and pick your spot."

"I thought you told him to hurry up."

"I'll just watch this race."

The jockey dismounted and started to walk his horse about. Some of the other jockeys brought their horses back in sympathy. The jockey remounted. His horse backed off and the race started without them. As the others approached the first fence the camera panned back to the horse at the start tapes, its jockey sitting quietly on its back. When the race was over Frank stood up and adjusted his muffler.

"I should have backed that, I fancied it. Come on, Neil."

He put his cap on in the mirror and glanced at the clock.

"Twenty-five to three. At one time I'd have been in the ground three quarters of an hour by now. Ta-ra love."

He kissed Shirley on the cheek and followed Neil out of the back door. They walked along the flags, up the entry, and waved to Shirley through the front window on their way up the street. From the top of the street they caught a bus into the town centre and when they got off at the terminus they had 15 minutes left before the kick off.

There was no crush in the streets leading to the ground, just a smattering of people walking in the same direction. Cars did not have to slow down, because no one was forced to walk in the road, and a trio of boys, waving rattles and scarves, was able to run swiftly and without interruption between the other pedestrians. When they ran past, Neil laughed and took his dad's hand.

"What are they doing that for, dad?"

"They're Town supporters. They're the Town colours, red and white."

"I know a boy with a scarf like that."

"Do you? I used to have one."

"Did you use to wave it like that?"

"I did when they scored. Do you know, when we used to come..."

"Did my mam come?"

"No, your mam never came. Before I knew your mam. Well, in them days these streets used to be packed, it was like being in the ground, and when the cars came they couldn't get past."

"What did they do?"

"They used to go ever so slow and blow their hooters, and everybody used to bang the sides and shout at them."

"Did you used to do that?"

"Sometimes, and sometimes when a gang got mad they used to rock a car and nearly turn it over."

"What did they do that for, dad?"

"Because they'd had a bit to drink, or if a driver was trying to go too fast, and just trying to force his way through them. It used to be a right carry on. I can remember somebody I knew, when he'd had a few pints and there was a jam on, setting off and running over the top of a line of cars, and all the drivers getting out of their cars when he'd gone, and shouting and cursing at him."

"Why did he do that, dad?"

"Well, because he was drunk and because he wanted a bit of fun."

They reached the top of the hill and the ground came into sight down the other side. As they approached it, men wearing armbands offered them programmes, official programmes. Every time they passed one of these men Neil turned and looked back at him.

"Why don't you buy one, dad?"

"I'm not bothered. You can have one if you want though, to show your mam."

"Can I, dad?"

Frank bought a programme but before giving it to Neil he opened it at the middle page and glanced at the teams. At inside left for the visitors: 'ROYLE'. He handed Neil the programme and as they crossed the road to the turnstiles Neil studied the cover. In a frame of advertisements, a footballer in the Town colours was kicking a ball.

There was no crowd outside the ground; just a policeman, a group of men in dark overcoats outside the ticket holders' turnstile, and a few people standing with their backs to the wall, waiting. From over the wall, the rhythm of a military band but no sound of people. Frank took Neil to the boys' turnstile and told him to wait at the other side. Neil looked through it and shook his head.

"I want to go with you, dad."

"I'm going through this next one. I'll see you at the other side."

"Why can't I come with you?"

"Because that turnstile's for misters, and that one's for little boys. Look, other little boys are going in."

Frank gave him a shilling and they stood and watched the boys go in. But Neil wouldn't.

"Oh, come on Neil, stop being so silly. What do you think I'm going to do, run away?"

Frank shook his arm and pushed him towards the turnstile.

"Neil, go home if you're going to be naughty."

Neil put one fist to his eyes and lowered his head. Frank pulled him close again and gave him a hug.

"Alright then, watch. I'll go in and when you see me through there, you come in."

Before Neil could answer, Frank left him, paid, and appeared a moment later at the other side of the Boys' turnstile. Neil paid, and they started along the back of the main stand towards the entrance to the terrace. When they passed the Players and Officials door Frank showed it to Neil.

"Look, that's where the players go in there. Do you want to go for a wee?"

Neil shook his head and continued to look at the Players and Officials door.

"You do, Neil, 'cos if you don't go now, you'll be wanting to go as soon as they've kicked off."

As Frank led him away a middle-aged man came out of the door walking with the aid of a stick.

"Is he a player, dad?"

"Who?"

Frank glanced at the men who were passing them at that moment but Neil pointed back towards the door.

"Him with the stick."

"That's the Town centre forward. He's injured, that's why he's using a walking stick."

Satisfied with this explanation, Neil let his father lead him quickly into the Gents.

When they walked round the end of the stand on to the terrace, Frank stopped on the top step and looked round. The ground was almost empty. There was a gathering behind each goal and the walls all round the pitch were lined, but in the stand it was like an afternoon showing at a cinema, and on the terrace there were spaces as large as badminton courts.

A record was playing over the Tannoy, a ballad of love and deep devotion. But in the rain and the cold, among the few indifferent spectators, the efforts of the vocalist were incongruous, and the fatuous quality of the lyric exposed.

"Who'd have thought it, walking in at ten to three and picking your spot? Where do you want to go?"

"Let's go near the front, dad."

"Come on then, let's go into the middle, then you can watch the players come out of the tunnel."

Frank led Neil towards the centre, walking down the terrace until they reached a barrier close to the tunnel and opposite the centre-line.

"This'll do, you can watch the players come out now."

He wiped the top of the barrier with his sleeve, then lifted Neil into a sitting position on top of it, supporting him with one arm across his back. The rest of the barrier was occupied by two youths. There was no one else standing within five yards of them.

Occasionally children would use the barrier as an obstacle in a chasing game, and as they dodged round it their excited cries carried up the terrace, up into the stand and echoed in the silence there. Neil watched them, smiling, as they ran about and when they ran up the terrace he turned round, and Frank had to hold on to him to stop him from falling.

"We have to go further back, we'll get wet here."

"No, let's stop here, dad."

Frank pulled Neil's hood well over his forehead, then he adjusted his own cap and looked round to see if there was room at the top of the terrace, where the roof of the stand sheltered the top few steps. There was plenty. Even the top step, where the wall of the stand offered a back rest, was not full.

"It's a big field, isn't it, dad?"

"It's a lovely field. It's a First Division pitch, that."

The grass down the centre of the pitch was worn and khaki-coloured, but there were expanses down both wings where the turf was as green and lush as a cricket field. Round the pitch, the track was churned up, and the red ash was patterned with studs and footprints. These prints were holding water and the continual puckering of their surfaces showed that the rain was still falling.

The wall surrounding the track was splashed and dirty. The whitewash had faded and the entire wall was given a grey appearance by thousands of ball marks printed on it: some overlapping to form fat eights, some fusing into dark fantastic blooms, and some isolated, perfect circles, with each panel clearly defined.

There was a feeble blossoming of red and white scarves on the Kop, accompanied by a rhythmic clapping, and the cry, 'TOWN!' But this display of loyalty was greeted with such apathy by the rest of the crowd, that the loyalists quickly became discouraged, and the whole sequence tailed off in confusion and embarrassment. Another record started. A newspaper seller appeared, advertising the two o'clock winner. He completed a full circuit of the pitch without selling one paper. Then the record stopped and a voice over the Tannoy announced the teams would be as per programme. Somebody cheered.

"They move their scarves like that when they play on television, don't they, dad?"

"They've usually something to move them about for though when they're on television."

"Why didn't we go and stand behind the goals, dad?"

"I don't know, I thought there might be a lot there. I thought you might not be able to see."

"There's a lot there now."

"There used to be that many five minutes after the gates had opened. Let me have a look at your programme, Neil."

"I want to get down, dad."

Frank lifted him down and Neil gave him the programme. On the page allocated to 'Today's Visitors' there was a head and shoulder portrait of Eddie Royle. It showed a thin faced youth with blonde hair bobbed up at the front. The headline was, 'Welcome back Eddie!' Frank folded the programme down the centre and showed Neil the photograph. Neil looked at it, then Frank started to read the article:

'This afternoon we extend a hearty welcome to someone who I am sure needs no introduction to loyal Town fans. I am talking of course about Eddie Royle, who I am sure you will agree has been one of the greatest players ever to don the famous red shirt of the Town, in all the long and distinguished history of the club. Eddie Royle was 'The toast of the Town,' a 'guest' in a great team, which, in three successive seasons were First Division Champions twice, and then in the following season F.A. Cup winners. A truly great team. Eddie set up the present club goalscoring record of 53 goals in a season. He also gained 33 international caps for England, and was said by many to be the greatest inside forward of his age.

'This afternoon is rather a special occasion for us, as I am sure it will be for Eddie, as this is the first time he has been back to Town Fields since those great and glorious years of success ... welcome home Eddie Royle! Our every good wish to you in the future (except for this afternoon's game of course!) and I am sure that many of our fans will join me in wishing that you were pulling the familiar red jersey of the Town over your head, where they feel in their hearts that you still belong.'

The Town came out. There was another burst of enthusiasm from the supporters on the Kop and all the children who had been playing up and down the terrace ran down to the wall and gave them a cheer.

The Town ran to the Kop end of the pitch and began to sprint and shoot, and practise set moves in twos and threes. Frank called Neil up from the wall and told him to watch the tunnel.

Eddie Royle came out first carrying a ball under one arm, walking slowly, and looking round the ground as he crossed the red ash. Somebody shouted 'Good old

Eddie!' and this single voice carried all over the ground. As soon as they were across the red ash the line of players following him broke up and they all ran past him towards the goal at the covered end. Eddie threw the ball to one of them and continued his walk. Frank bent down, close to Neil's head and pointed him out.

"Which one, dad?"

"Him with the fair hair."

"Which one?"

"Him rubbing his hands together."

"Do you mean that bald 'un?"

"He's not bald. It's because he's got fair hair."

Eddie did not kick in with the same vigour as the rest of the team. He exchanged a few passes and chipped a few centres across, but he never called or clapped his hands for a ball. He appeared disinterested in the whole proceedings and when the official appeared, he immediately detached himself and walked towards the centre.

"Who's captain of the Town, dad?"

"I don't know. Here, have a look in the programme."

One of the youths sharing the barrier with them, turned and told them:

"Corrigan."

Corrigan won the toss and elected to play as they were. The referee blew his whistle to attract the attention of the players and both teams spread themselves out according to their positions. When Eddie Royle took up his position he made Frank smile. He adopted the orthodox position-ing of an inside forward, close to the centre forward, but instead of facing the goal he was due to attack, he stood facing his own players.

Frank pointed this out to Neil and told him that Eddie had always stood like that at the kick off. Even when he had played for England, he had stood like that. When they showed the international matches on the News at the pictures they used to wait for the teams to line up, and watch for Eddie, and when he took up his position and then turned round and showed his opponents the big number 10 on his back, they cheered in the pictures. They would nudge each other, and sit up and look across at each other. 'Good old Eddie,' they shouted, as he stood there, knees flexing slowly, head bowed, fingers walking gently across the backs of his hands as if they were cold — even though it was an international at the end of the season, and the sun was shining, the players casting shadows across the turf.

One of the youths stepped back from the barrier and shouted:

"Hey up, one of theirs is playing for us."

He got a few laughs. Neil laughed. Frank turned to him sharply:

"I wish he was."

The youth said something to his mate and they both laughed. The referee blew his whistle and the centre forward touched the ball to Eddie and sprinted away from him. Eddie turned with it on the outside of his boot, dragged it away from a tackle and clipped a long high pass down the centre of the pitch. The Town centre half backed away to get underneath the ball but it was beating him all the time, and it dropped behind him, leaving the centre forward with a clear run at goal. He shot too soon and the ball went over the crossbar into the Kop. The crowd went 'Ooo!' Frank looked along the barrier at the youths but they were shouting at the centre half for missing the ball. Eddie Royle was still standing in the centre circle.

The next time he received the ball he was tackled hard and the force of it knocked him down. The youths cheered. Frank gripped the barrier hard and stood up straight, red in the face.

"Foul! You big dirty sod!"

Neil looked up at his dad and round at the other people who were looking at him. The youths turned on him.

"What do you mean, dirty? There was nothing wrong with that tackle."

"He only went straight over the ball, that's all."

"Oh, give up mister. He was too slow. He got caught with the ball."

Eddie was caught again and the Town scored.

"What did I tell you! He's a mile too slow! He's had it!"

Frank pointed, and blamed the defence for bad covering. Neil was cheering the goal with the rest of the children down at the wall. Frank brushed some flakes of rust off his coat sleeve.

"They want to get these barriers painted. It's a bloody disgrace, this ground."

"Up the Town!" one of the youths shouted.

Eddie found a space, clapped his hands for the pass, received it, and angled it straight back into the space behind the defender for his own player to run on to. But the player had stopped once he had given his pass and the defender was able to turn and retrieve the ball. Eddie turned his back and walked away.

"Rubbish! Bad ball, Royle!"

Frank whipped round on them.

"Bad ball! You two have about as much idea about football as that bloody…"

As he glanced round for a suitable simile, a dog trotted past with Neil and some more children after it. Frank pointed at it.

"…as that bloody dog."

The dog passed by, occasionally glancing back at its pursuers, easily maintaining its lead over them. They all watched it go, then turned back to the match, and their argument.

"Haven't you ever heard of the wall-pass, you two? If that half back had have kept going, he'd have got that ball back straight at his feet."

"He passed it to nobody."

"Only because the other bloke stopped. It wouldn't have gone to nobody if he'd have kept running."

"What do you think he is, a mind reader?"

"He didn't have to be a mind reader, it was the obvious pass."

"It was a bad ball. He's had it, Royle. He ought to have packed it in years since."

Eddie drifted to the wing and held his hand up for the ball. By the time it was delivered, not only was he marked, but the pass was directed yards behind him, so he had to turn and chase with the defender coming up fast behind. As soon as he reached the ball he was tackled and both he and the ball were bundled into touch. The ball bounced off the wall and stopped on the red ash. As Eddie walked across to pick it up, one of the youths shouted down:

"Rubbish Royle! A mile too slow!"

Eddie did not even look up into the terrace. He placed his foot under the ball, trapped it between his instep and his shin, and lifted it up into his hands, ready to take the throw in. Neil ran up from the wall and jumped for Frank to bend down, so that he could whisper into his ear.

"He came right close to me then, dad."

"That's Eddie Royle."

"And all his shorts were muddy from tumbling down."

"There's no wonder, the hammer they're giving him."

The youths laughed. The Town scored again and after they had finished cheering, they began to chant, 'Easy! Easy!' One of them winked, the other smiled, and they began to converse in loud voices which were out of proportion to the distance separating them.

"I thought this Royle reckoned to be a good player, then."

"There's no wonder the Town let him go. I bet they had to give him away."

But Frank was not listening. He had lost sight of Neil.

He leaned over the barrier and looked along the wall, but he was not there; while he was looking at the back of the terrace the Town scored their third goal. At the roar, Frank spun round but all he saw was the left winger turning away from goal and the goalkeeper on the floor looking at the ball behind him. Then Neil was at Frank's side, pulling his sleeve.

"That was a good goal, wasn't it, dad?"

"Where have you been?"

The smile and excitement went out of Neil's face and he stepped away from Frank.

"I've only been up there."

He nodded towards the back of the terrace. Frank glanced round, then turned back to the game, still angry.

"Well stop running about, else you'll get lost."

"I'll not, dad, I could see you all the time."

"Well stop here now then."

At half-time the Town were still leading three-nil. The small boys on the terrace ran to the tunnel to watch the players go in. When Eddie Royle passed, somebody booed. Frank shouted:

"Hard luck, Eddie!"

The boys ignored him but when the Town players came in they cheered and hung over the tunnel walls, trying to pat them on the back. When all the players and officials, trainers, substitutes and ball boys had disappeared up the tunnel, a record came on. People began to walk about and look around, and on the terrace they turned and leaned with their backs to the barriers, and

looked up to see who was in the stand, or to see if anything was happening there. Frank pulled Neil's hood up
and wiped his nose for him.

"Are you enjoying it, son?"

Neil nodded and jumped up on to the barrier, his
stomach across the bar, his upper body hanging down on
the other side.

"Watch this dad, this is what we do at school."

He ducked his head and went over the top, hanging
onto the barrier and finishing in a crouching position underneath it.

"Neil, be careful."

"It's easy, dad."

"Look at your coat now."

Where Neil's coat had rubbed against the barrier, it
was stained and flecked with rust. Frank tried to clean it
with his hand but after he had finished it was still dirty,
and there were rust flakes sticking to the wet black fuzz
of the wool.

"You'll not half cop it, lad, when your mam sees that"

"I'm hungry, dad."

"What do you want?"

One of the youths from the barrier came along the
terrace, concentrating hard on two steaming plastic cups
of Bovril. He was walking too fast and one of the cups
slopped over. He stopped, allowed the liquid to settle,
then continued at a slower pace. When he arrived at the
barrier, he handed the cup which had spilled to his mate.
Then he took a Cornish pasty out of his pocket, shook the

greaseproof paper from it and bit into the pastry. Steam rose from round his mouth and he had to snuffle at the pasty to stop the hot gravy from running down his chin.

"I want one of them, dad."

"Here, go and fetch one then."

He offered Neil the money but he would not take it.

"I don't know where you get them from."

"There's a stall, round the back of the stand, where we came in."

"You go, dad."

"I'm not going, Neil. Look, you go straight on there. I'll watch you. I can see you right to the end. Then it's just round the back. I'll watch you."

Neil hesitated and Frank pretended to put his money away. Neil took the money and Frank watched him walk the full length of the terrace and move out of sight round the end of the stand.

The half-time scores went up. Frank tried to look at the programme of the nearest youth to see who was winning two-nil. Some of the scores raised a flicker of interest and men would turn and tell strangers that Manchester United were losing one-nil, then go back to their programmes. Frank looked for Neil; he was halfway along the terrace, Bovril in one hand, Cornish pasty in the other. When he arrived he gave Frank the change and bit into the pasty.

"Let's have a look at your programme, Neil."

He took the programme out of Neil's pocket and turned to the half-time scores.

"Liverpool's winning, Neil. Manchester United's

losing one nil at home. They should win though. Spurs are only drawing."

He looked at the First Division scores and pushed the programme back into Neil's pocket. When the players started to straggle out for the second half, Neil gave Frank the remains of the pasty and the Bovril, and ran down to the tunnel to watch them. Frank finished off the pasty, washed it down with the Bovril and dropped the cup. As it landed he half-volleyed it into the bottom of the terrace.

The nearest youth nudged his mate.

"Hey up, Eddie Royle's here."

They both laughed and were still elaborating on the joke when Eddie Royle scored. The right winger dribbled round his full back and cut in for goal. The Town goalkeeper ran out to intercept him and the wingman drove the ball hard and low past him across the face of the goal. Both attackers and defenders tried to reach it but it was travelling too fast and when it looked as if it was going to run out of play, and the crowd had already started to 'oooo', Eddie Royle appeared at the far post and side footed into the goal. He followed the ball in, picked it up off the little lawn in the back of the net and threw it to the goalkeeper, who was getting to his feet on the corner of the six yard box.

Frank took his cap off and waved it. He was the only one on the terrace cheering and people smiled and remarked about it. He fixed his cap back on and turned to the youths.

"See that."

"See what? Anybody could have scored that. It would have been harder to miss. He just happened to be in the right place, that's all."

Frank slapped the barrier, making the metal ring and the rust fall. The ringing vibrated along the hollow pipe and came out loud at both ends.

"That's the point, he was in the right place. See the rest of his forwards, sliding and stretching for it? Eddie was there though, waiting for it. He knew."

"Give up mister, anybody could have scored that."

"I know they could but anybody didn't. Eddie Royle scored it."

"He happened to be there, that's all."

"He was always there. That's why he was such a great player."

"I'm glad you said *was*, mister."

"He can still do a bit now. He's still a mile too good for this league."

"Oh, give up! He's had it, he's finished. He ought to be drawing his pension by now."

"Talk sense, lad! Anyway, what do you know about football? You've never seen any football down here. You've watched this third division stuff that long that you've no idea what good football's about."

"And I suppose you have?"

Frank moved along the barrier to them, so close that anybody seeing them converse but unable to hear the conversation, would have thought that they were friends.

"Listen lad, when I was your age the greatest team in

the land used to play on that pitch, not a collection of rubbing rags like this lot. We were brought up on good football. We saw the best here. All the greats. You mention
them, and we saw them. This ground used to be packed
every week. At work they talked of nothing else from
one weekend to another but football. This town was
football daft. And when they played away, you used to
get thousands following them. We used to travel all over
the country to support them."

And Frank told them about the places that he and his
mates had been to. How they used to parade through the
centres in their scarves and rosettes, shouting and laughing, and then they would go to a pub and stay there until
it was time for the match. When it was a new town they
would mill around outside the pub, flushed and red eyed
and ask people in loud voices the way to the ground, and
when they were told, they would tell the informant that
the Town would thrash them. Frank and his mates went
to Wembley. They saved up for it and went down on
Friday and stayed at a hotel in King's Cross. They went
drinking and in every pub they complained about the
beer, saying it wasn't a patch on the beer back home.

They visited Piccadilly Circus and Trafalgar Square
and every few hours they ate large fried meals at Forte's
or Lyons. They visited Soho and read the advertisements.
They looked at the stills outside the strip clubs and
debated whether to go in and promised to go in the next
time they came down. And all through the West End
every sight was worth a comment and a laugh, and when

a barman or a waiter joked about the match, they always mentioned Eddie Royle, and shouted 'Up the Town!'

And then they went to Wembley. None of them had a ticket but they all bought one at the black market price outside the ground. When they had bought them, they stood quietly for a few seconds looking at, and fingering their tickets. They bought programmes, rosettes and full colour pictures of the Town, and when they went through the turnstiles they all kept the portion to be retained, and tucked it safely away in an inside pocket. They were in the ground at half past one. They applauded the gymnastic display and the marching musicians. They sang every song and passed a bottle of whiskey round from mouth to mouth. The teams came out and Frank went quiet, and tears came into his eyes when he saw the Town, their new red shirts and white shorts shining in the sun, against the brilliant green of the clean turf. And he was there to see it all. To see the Town presented to the Queen. To see the Queen stop and speak with Eddie, and to see Eddie nod his head and smile, and then have a good look at the Queen after she had gone by, and was shaking hands with the next player.

Eddie Royle scored the first goal. Frank leapt straight onto the back of one of his mates and they both went down in the crowd. The rest of their mates leapt onto them. They all lay hugging each other, laughing and crying in a heap.

They were there at the reception, when the Town brought the cup home, and the town centre was packed.

They were always there. At every home match for three seasons Frank was there. Into the pub at lunch time, a few pints, then off to Town Fields. And after the Town had won (they nearly always won at home), hurrying home in the dark, the fog, the rain, in time for *Sports Report* and his tea. His mother telling him to get his wet things off. The house spotless and smelling of baking. His brother and his brother's fiancée for tea, and his dad asking him who'd won, and poking the fire for him to come and have a warm, even though the fire was stacked up and blazing, and the tops of the flames were out of sight up the chimney. And after tea all sitting round the fire, then getting changed, best suit and clean white shirt, and meeting his mates again for another session before the dance. And after the dance, whatever his luck, there was another whole day left before Monday.

Royle scored his second goal. Even the two youths applauded this one. The right winger ran past the Town left back, ran the ball to the goal line and centred. The ball curved away, behind the centre forward, and even as he turned to remonstrate with his wingman, it fell into the stride of Eddie Royle who crisply half-volleyed it into the goal.

The goalkeeper was in position and ready for the shot. He saw the centre, he saw Eddie time his run onto the ball, and he saw the ball leave Eddie's boot. A photograph in the local newspaper on Monday morning recorded this alertness: eyes on the shooter, hands at the ready and knees slightly flexed in the characteristic crouch of goalkeepers. But in the photograph the ball was behind him, Eddie was following through, his head still down, and the centre forward was caught in profile, his mouth open in anger at something out of the picture. The power of the shot had also tested the reflexes of the crowd behind the goal. Only a few faces had begun to react. Mouths were beginning to open, one boy had his arm half raised, and there was the occasional transitional smile that a second later would have bloomed into the full grin. But most of the faces were still passive, as though the ball was in midfield, or it had just gone out of play for a throw in.

Eddie turned round and thumped his fist into his palm, the first time he had shown any emotion during the game. The crowd applauded and Frank cheered and nudged the nearest youth incessantly on the arm.

"See that? See that for a goal? I thought he'd had it. I thought you said he'd had it!"

The youth told his mate to move up the barrier so he could get away from Frank's elbow. As soon as there was space between them Frank stopped shouting and looked for Neil, the elation still in his face.

Three-two, it was a game again, and the crowd began to encourage the Town as Eddie Royle's team worked hard for the equaliser. Frank could not see Neil anywhere. He watched the game for a minute, then his eyes wandered from the pitch, and he looked around, stepping back, and moving in front of the barrier to see different sections of the terrace. Any heightened reaction from the crowd whipped his eyes back to the field of play, but always too late, so he missed.

He searched for Neil with increasing fury, moving further away from the barrier, then returning to it to see if Neil had come back. Then the Town scored. The youths bounced up and down behind the barrier, pushing themselves off the bar to gain greater height. Frank waited until the game had re-started and they had settled down, then turned to them.

"Did any of you two see where my little lad went?"

They shook their heads, glanced round in a perfunctory manner, then went back to the game, congratulating, abusing and advising, according to who had possession of the ball.

"Will you do me a favour, then? I'm going to look for him. If he comes back, will you tell him to stop here and not move 'til I come back?"

"We'll tell him."

Frank set off slowly along the terrace. There were only a few hundred people in this half and when he reached the end he knew Neil was not among them. He walked up the steps towards the corner of the stand and as he turned round Eddie Royle received the ball on the touchline below him. The Town left back came to challenge him and the two players became isolated, yards away from anyone else on the pitch. There were no spectators down by the wall in that corner and it seemed as though the two players were involved in a private contest, on a private pitch. The full back, eyes on the ball, crouched for the tackle, waiting for Eddie to make his move. Eddie looked for someone to come and help him but no one came and he was left there, trapped in the corner. They stood there, two yards apart. Eddie kept feigning, and swaying, and sweeping his foot over the ball, but he could not unbalance his opponent or induce him to make the tackle. Frank started to walk down the terrace.

"Go on Eddie, take him on, lad. Show him."

But there was no decisive move from either of the players. Frank moved closer, encouraging Eddie all the time.

"You can beat him, Eddie. He's rubbish."

He leaned on the wall, his head level with their legs, and watched Eddie tap the ball from foot to foot. He watched the left boot swing over the ball but leave the ball stationery. He could see the bows in Eddie's laces and the tie ups where the turn-over of the sock had worked up. He could see the scratches on the orange leather of the ball and he could hear the breathing of both players as they waited.

"Go on Eddie, show him who's boss."

Eddie shoved the ball between the full back's legs and sprinted, but the full back turned, beat him to the ball, and started to dribble it up field. Eddie chased him for a few yards, then stopped and stood there, hands on hips, panting, steam rising from his shirt, and the dampness of the shirt stuck to his body, revealing the thickness of his trunk. He wiped his face with his sleeve and flattened the wet sticks of hair back into place across the bald crown. Coughing and hawking, he started to walk slowly up the field in pursuit of the ball.

Frank walked back up the terrace, paused for a final look along it, then ambled round the back of the stand. Neil was standing in front of the refreshment stall with another boy. When Frank saw him he started to walk quickly towards him.

"Neil! Neil!"

Neil looked round and ran to his father. Frank gripped him by the shoulder, shook him, then bent down and started to slap his backside.

"I've been looking all over for you, you little bugger! Where you been? I thought I told you to stop with me."

Neil was crying and trying to break free but Frank held him hard by the forearm. Each time he slapped him, they rotated. The other boy and the woman behind the counter were the only witnesses. They both watched in silence. There was a roar from the other side of the stand and the boy started to run along the back of the stand. Frank stopped hitting Neil and dragged him in the same direction. They reached the terrace as the visiting team were kicking off. Eddie Royle had taken up his customary stance, facing his own team but the centre forward passed to the other inside forward, so Eddie turned round and moved up the field.

Frank did not go back to the barrier near the tunnel but stayed in the corner, near the high railings which divided the Kop from the terrace. Neil stood on the step below him, leaning on the railings, sniffling, fists up over his face. When Town scored again, he lowered his fists and Frank stepped down to him and wiped his face with his handkerchief. Frank gave him a hug and asked if he wanted to stop for the players' autographs. Neil shook his head. People started to leave.

At the end, Frank watched Eddie Royle leave the pitch, then he took Neil by the hand and they moved on. There were only a few people in front of them going up the hill which led away from the ground. When they were over the top of the hill Frank asked Neil if he had enjoyed it and if he would like to come again. Neil looked up at him and nodded.

"Can I, dad?"

Frank smiled and told him he would bring him again sometime and that he would soon be big enough to come with his own pals. Frank started to trot, still holding Neil by the hand.

"Come on, let's run. We might be in time for *Sports Report*."

A bit further on, Neil looked up at Frank again.

"Dad?"

"What?"

"What's it mean, hot-spurs?"

Playing in Sand

I was playing in sand.
The first real heap I'd ever seen.
My mother liked it too.
Such a change from muck.
All she did was beat my clothes
And they were clean again.

They were building prefabs.
Nineteen forty-six.
We were driving roads
For Dinky Toys
While workmen caused subsidence
With their shovels.

Then the miners started trooping past.
A lot.
Like an exit from a football match.
But quiet.
As though their team had lost.

But it was tea time.
The wrong time for coming home.
Even then I knew the shift endings,
My mother's anxious glances at the clock.
The bustle in her movements
When he did not come.

Go and see if he's coming
She used to say.
The kettle on,
The potatoes bubbling on the hob.
Too busy to go out
And look down the empty street herself.

"Doug Westerman's been killed."
We kept on building,
Busily closing cracks
And complaining to the labourer
Who laughed at us,
And kept on portioning sand into the mixer.

When I got home
My mother had her head down, crying,
My father, still in his pit muck,
Stood stiff as a flue-brush by her side.
Your grandad's been killed he said.
In a fall. An accident.

My grandad?
Doug Westerman!
It hadn't clicked
I was only six.
He had no name
He was just my grandad then.

My father washed his hands
And made my tea.

Barry with Richard in Blackpool.

Black, from the wrists up
With his sleeves rolled up,
He looked as though
He was cutting bread in gloves.

I ate quickly and went out.
Back to the sand with my racing car.
It was better now
The workmen had knocked off.
We could build properly,
Tunnel carefully,
In peace.

Clem Thomas

Clem Thomas was the most famous player ever to play for the Albion. Old Albion supporters argued there had been players as good as Clem Thomas, but even they had to agree that there had been none more famous. Clem Thomas played centre forward for the Albion. He also played centre forward for England, and for both teams he scored goals, many goals. Season after season, he scored more goals than any other player in the country.

Clem was the most valuable player in the country. A new transfer record would have been established if he had changed clubs but he never wanted to change clubs. He was an Albion man. The Albion had signed him straight from school and he had been proud to join them. They had nursed him and guided his progress carefully, and he had progressed smoothly through the Albion junior teams, at the same time gaining representative honours and recognition with the young England teams. He made his debut for the Albion at 18, for England at 19, and he was now a local legend and national figure.

When he married a local beauty queen the city-centre was blocked and the event was featured in most of the national newspapers. Clem appeared on television advertisements, a whole range of football clothing and footwear bore his name, and he had other business interests, outside football. He lived out of the city, near Rockdene Golf Club in an area so silent that it seemed as if the residents were perpetually away on holiday. And when he drove into the city on his way to the ground, people recognised his big white car, and at traffic lights bent down to look and wave at him through the window.

Clifford Tagg idolised Clem Thomas. He went to watch Clem rather than the Albion, and at home he spent much of his spare time compiling scrapbooks devoted exclusively to the career of his idol. Every match report, magazine article, or newspaper story with a reference to the Albion centre forward was carefully cut out and pasted into the exercise books, along with the many photographs illustrating Clem Thomas' prowess as a scorer of goals, both with his head and feet.

He had to keep these books hidden because if they were found while he was out, or at work, they were invariably destroyed: his father ripped the pages out and used them for betting slips; his mother stuck them on the rail behind the toilet door; and if his younger brothers or sisters found them, according to their ages, they either tore the pages out or chewed the covers, or scribbled all over the cuttings and defaced the photographs. But hiding them was difficult in a small house, without a room of his own, a wardrobe of his own, or even a drawer in a bureau of his own.

He had tried keeping them at work, in a box, in the corner of the shop where he hung his jacket and stored his sweeping brushes. But there was always someone looking into the box and taking the books out, and leaving oily fingerprints all over the covers and pages. Or they would hide them under the benches among machine parts, or behind lathes and drills, and Clifford would spend hours looking for them while the metal waste from the machines collected on the floor. Then the foreman would notice and shout at him, telling him to get cracking with his brush.

When Clifford found his books they were always crumpled and smeared with grease and when he tried to wipe the dirt off with his handkerchief he only spread the stains further.

Clifford came from the same part of the city as Clem, and Clem's parents still lived a few streets away. Clifford had attended the same school, Brewer Street Secondary Modern, had sat in the same classrooms, perhaps the same desks, and they had both left from form 4C. Clifford once asked the teachers about Clem but only one remained from Clem's day, and all he said was that Clem Thomas' brains were in his boots.

Clifford went to the match early to watch the players arrive, with his scrapbooks in his hand. When Clem Thomas arrived, Clifford joined the throng round him, clamouring for his autograph, looking up at him, trying to touch him and rub up against him. The boys who had got Clem Thomas' autograph stood back and waited for the other players. All the other autograph hunters were much younger than Clifford, many of them still in short trousers. The regulars knew him and asked him to show them his scrap books. When Clifford proudly turned the pages full of Clem Thomas, and Clem Thomas' autographs, they nudged each other, and smirked, and exclaimed in feigned awe.

He stood back when the visiting team arrived in their coach. The other boys became excited and ran up, pointing at the windows to the players they recognised, and when the door was slid open they crowded round. The players had to push their way through, some smiling and signing books, others serious, thrusting them aside. When the players had gone in, Clifford ran around to the Kop end with the boys, paid, ran up the steps and down the empty terracing to the wall at the front, where he shoved and argued with the others for a place directly behind the goal. While he waited for the teams to come out, he scoured the programme for information or photographs of Clem. He studied Clem's goalscoring record and then bought a newspaper and went through that for anything further that could have developed since the programmes were printed.

Clem always came out last in the line of players and Clifford saved his cheer until he appeared. The Albion came down to the Kop end to kick in and when the captains tossed up the Albion lost the toss and had to play towards the Kop in the first half.

From the start it was obvious the Albion were going to have a good day. They settled down at once, attacked, and their moves were immediately fluent, their passing precise, their shooting dangerous. In the building of these attacks there appeared to be nothing exceptional about Clem Thomas' game. His passing was accurate but not as piercingly destructive as that of Ian Cliff at inside left. Both wingmen looked better running with the ball at their feet, and the control and close dribbling of Roy Clay, the inside right, was far superior to anything in Clem's repertoire. But it was in and around the penalty area that his talent was instantly recognisable. In this area of the field Clem Thomas was peerless. Every time he received the ball he appeared capable of scoring, because whatever distance, angle or opposition, his effort was positive. He was a goalscoring genius. It was as though the whole meaning of his life was distilled into those few moments when he received a pass, controlling and shooting with perfect timing, the swift movement flawless in its execution; or when he rose to a centre with the power flowing up from the legs to the arching back through the neck to the striking head, which sent the ball towards goal with the force of a boot.

When he did these things it was as if no one else was on the field, as if a spotlight had been turned on Clem, causing the rest of the players to fade into shadows. And when he scored these goals it was exciting and the excitement was contagious. The spectators wanted to embrace Clem and thank him personally and reverentially for the experience.

The Albion scored after four minutes when Clem shot so forcefully that the goalkeeper could only knock the ball to Roy Clay, who immediately volleyed past him. Scores of boys ran onto the pitch and danced round Roy and any other Albion players they could catch. Clifford stayed behind the wall, cheering and laughing, then urging them on as they outran the police and came tumbling back over the wall, burrowing their way into the protective ranks of the crowd.

Before the game re-started there was an announcement over the Tannoy, stating that anyone else caught running onto the pitch would be immediately ejected from the ground. The crowd booed. The referee blew his whistle and a minute later Clem scored. He called for a square ball, received it, and immediately his head was down, body poised, and the shot dispatched sweetly and economically into the goal. So easy, yet he was 25 yards out, and closely marked. Clifford was straight over the wall, running for Clem. Before the police could start to chase, he was at Clem's side, pulling his sleeve and patting his back, feeling the white number nine standing up in relief on the red material. Clifford was the only supporter who had run onto the pitch. The crowd was cheering the goal, the Albion players were congratulating Clem, and Clifford was there on the pitch among them, congratulating him with them, while all around them, the noise went on and on and on. A policeman grabbed him. He did not try to escape. Another one held his other arm and he was led away, looking back over his shoulder at Clem, who was walking to the centre with his team-mates. They reached the track, and the crowd

booed, and whistled and called obscenities to the policemen all the way round to the tunnel. Clifford appeared
oblivious and kept his eyes on the pitch.

It was dark and quiet under the stand and the noise of
the crowd seemed distant. Then they were across the
corridor of the Players and Officials door. The policemen
pushed Clifford roughly out into the street and went
back inside. He walked about outside the ground for a
while, trying to interpret the game from the reactions of
the crowd. He soon tired of this and drifted away. He
went into the city centre and wandered round the
market. He went home, tuned in the radio and waited
for *Sports Report*.

Immediately after the signature tune, the main headline was that the Albion had won 9−2, and that Clem
Thomas had scored eight goals, to set a new individual
goalscoring record for a First Division match.

In the Paper

I read in the paper
Where a man
Had appealed against death.
They allowed him
Twenty-six words
In one square inch.

Over the page,
An advert struck.
One full page they took
To state their case.

But they could offer money
For this space.
The man could give them nothing
But his life.

The Turnstile Man

Ralph scraped the last shreds of fish from the skin, collected them onto his fork with the last chip, then leaned over and placed the plate on the floor. Still bent over, he snapped his fingers and called to the cat lying on its side in front of the fire.

"Jackie. Come on, Jackie."

Without moving its body, the cat raised its head and looked over its shoulder at him. It got up and walked over to the plate. It sniffed at the fish, settled down over it and began to eat, turning its head to one side as it bit through the skin. Ralph scratched it between the shoulder blades, then shoved his chair back from the table and stood up.

"Jackie Moon's just like our Jackie, mam. When he dives and saves a shot like a cat."

Ralph performed a little sideways leap and clutched at an imaginary ball. The cat looked up at this sudden movement. Ralph's mother continued to file her nails on the settee. Ralph walked over to her and tried to drag his jacket out from underneath her. She had to bounce up and down until he got it out.

"Can I have some money, mam?"

"I thought I gave you some?"

"You gave me sixpence for school yesterday."

"I don't know, you must think I'm made of money."

She picked up her handbag from beside her and took out her purse.

"How much do you want?"

"Two bob."

"Two bob? It's not that much to go in, is it?"

"It's a shilling to go in but I want a programme and some money for sweets."

She looked in her purse and nudged some coins about in the two compartments.

"I haven't got two bob."

"Oh mam, everybody says that."

"I can't help that. I've only got a note and you're not taking that."

She gave him a shilling and a sixpence.

"That's all I've got in change. You'll have to get some more off your dad if you see him."

Ralph lowered his head and closely studied the shilling piece, turning it over and over on his palm as though it was the first time he had ever seen such a coin.

"If I see him, mam, have I to tell him owt?"

"What do you mean?"

"I just wondered if there was owt you wanted me to tell him."

"You can tell him owt you like for all I care."

She zipped her purse, threw it into her handbag and snapped it shut. Ralph turned away and walked to the door.

135

"Have you got your key, Ralph?"

Ralph felt his chest and, through his shirt, fingered the shape of the key which was hanging by a piece of string round his neck.

"And if I'm not in at tea time, there's some tea in the pantry for you."

Ralph turned round, his hand still on the door knob.

"You're not working again are you, mam?"

"No, but I might go out."

"Where to?"

"Shopping."

"Well, you'll be back if you're only going shopping, won't you?"

"I haven't decided yet. Anyway, never you mind where I'm going."

Ralph turned away and started to cry.

"Now what's the matter with you?"

"You're never in, you."

"Well, I can't stop in and go out to work as well, can I?"

"I know, but you never stop in when you're not at work."

"I've got to have some pleasure, Ralph. Now stop crying and come here and let's wipe your face."

Keeping his back to her, Ralph wiped his eyes on his sleeve and opened the door.

"And if I'm not in, Ralph, don't be waiting up for me."

Ralph slammed the door and sprinted furiously up the street.

He was still panting when he reached Alan's house. Alan's mother answered his knock and told him to come in. Alan was stretched out in front of the fire reading a comic; his father was sitting in his overalls, having his dinner, his face still dirty from work. He looked up at Ralph and winked at him.

"Hey up then, Ralph. Who's going to win today, then?"

"City."

"No chance. They'll get murdered."

Ralph smiled and lowered his head shyly.

"Fancy a bet then, Ralph? I'll give you the City and the draw."

Alan's mother, helping him on with his coat, smiled at Ralph.

"Take no notice of him, Ralph, he's only teasing you."

Alan looked at Ralph closely, for the first time.

"What you been crying for?"

Ralph blushed and lowered his head again.

"I haven't been crying."

"You have, all your face's dirty with tears."

"Them's not tears. It's sweat with running."

Alan turned to his mother for confirmation.

"Hasn't he been crying, mam?"

"Alan, stop arguing."

She pulled his bobble cap down over his ears and tightened his blue and white supporter's scarf.

"Can I have some money, mam?"

"How much do you want?"

Alan turned to Ralph again.

"How much you got, Ralph?"

"Half a crown."

"Can I have half a crown, like Ralph, mam?"

Alan's dad pushed his empty plate away from him and reached for his cigarettes.

"You're going early enough, aren't you? They'll not have opened the gates yet."

The boys looked at each other and grinned.

"What are you two grinning about?"

"Nowt, are we, Ralph?"

Then, still looking at Ralph, Alan spoke to his father.

"Dad, you know Ralph's dad?"

Ralph stepped further into the room and shook his head.

"Don't Alan, we said that it was going to be a secret."

Alan turned his back on him and went over to the table.

"You know Ralph's dad? He works in the turnstiles down at the City."

"Is that right, Ralph? I'll go and find him this afternoon then, and see about getting in free."

"That's what Ralph does, dad. His dad gets him in free every week. He lets him climb over the turnstile."

"He does right. Think he'll let me climb over, Ralph?"

Ralph smiled but was still frowning at Alan.

"You shouldn't tell anybody, Alan. He said he'd get into trouble if anybody knew."

"That's why we're going early, dad. Ralph's going to try and get me in as well."

He took a biscuit off the table. His mother gave Ralph one and shoved a block of chocolate into Alan's pocket as they went out.

"Give Ralph a bit of that. And don't be getting into trouble."

As they walked away from the house she opened the door and shouted up the street after them:

"And come straight home after, Alan."

As soon as she had gone back inside, Ralph admonished Alan for giving away their secret. He said he had only told him because he had promised not to tell anyone; his dad would get the sack if anybody found out. Alan told him that it didn't matter because his dad wouldn't tell.

There was no crowd outside the ground; it was too early. A group of boys were waiting at the Players' Entrance with autograph books and albums, and two programme sellers were standing talking nearby. In the centre of the street a mounted policeman was talking to a bobby. They laughed, the mountie nudged his horse and it walked away, clipping the asphalt with its shoes. The turnstiles were open but along the full length of the main stand there was no clank-clank from any of them to disturb the quiet.

Ralph and Alan tried all the turnstiles along the main stand. Then they turned the corner and tried the Spion Kop end. Ralph's father was in the second turnstile they came to. Ralph told Alan to wait while he went to ask.

"Hello, dad."

His dad looked down at him and smiled.

"Hello, Ralph. How you going on, then?"

He put his hand through the mouse-hole in the wire guard and ruffled Ralph's hair. Below the mouse-hole the iron counter had been worn shiny by the repeated scraping of coins. The rest of the counter was painted blue, but in places the paint was flaking off and the exposed metal was dirty and pitted with rust.

"Are you alright then, Ralph? Everything alright at home?"

Ralph nodded and picked at the paint with his nails.

"I thought you said you were coming to see us, dad?"

"I am."

"You said you were coming last week."

"I said I'd come sometime, I didn't say last week."

"You promised."

"How's your mam, Ralph?"

"She's alright."

"Is she working today?"

"No, but she's going out though."

Ralph pushed against the turnstile. It gave a little, then held. He pushed again, hard.

"You can't come in that way, Ralph. It'd record if I let you through. Be quick and climb over."

"You're coming home again, aren't you, dad?"

His dad fingered the neat stacks of coins beside him on the counter: silver and copper, each stack built of similar coins.

"'Course I am, Ralph. How's Jackie going on? Is he still licking his jersey clean?"

They both laughed, then a customer arrived and Ralph had to step back to let him through. He paid, the turnstile clanked, and Ralph's father added the two coins to the appropriate piles.

"Come on, Ralph. Climb over then, before anybody sees you."

"Dad, I've brought Alan with me. Can he come over as well? I said that you would."

"Alan who?"

"Alan Dixon. Can he, dad?"

"I thought it was a secret."

"I've only told Alan. He lets me go and play in their house at nights, so it's only fair."

"You'll be getting me the sack. Come on, be quick."

Ralph dodged back outside and called Alan. They quickly scrambled over the turnstile and jumped down inside the ground. Alan wanted to go straight away but Ralph hung back to speak to his father again. Alan went to buy a programme.

"I haven't told anybody else, dad."

"That's a good lad. Have you got enough money?"

"I've got one and six. My mam hadn't got any more."

"No, she'll have plenty tonight though, you can bet."

"I haven't told her that you let me in free."

"And you don't want to either, else she'll say that she's got nowt at all the next time you want to come."

He felt in his jacket pocket, sorted through some change and gave Ralph half a crown.

"Ta, dad."

Alan called to him from the steps which led to the top of the Kop and beckoned to him with his programme.

"Come on, Ralph!"

"I'm coming!"

"Ta-ra then, Ralph. Be good, lad."

"I'll tell my mam that I've seen you and that you're coming to see us."

"Alright then."

"When, dad?"

"I can't say, love. But if I don't see you, I'll see you at the next home match. And don't tell anybody else, will you? Remember, it's a secret."

"I'll not, ta-ra, dad."

"Ta-ra, love."

Ralph left him, bought a programme, and ran up the steps to Alan, who was waiting for him at the top. Panting, he held out his hand.

"My dad's given me half a crown, look."

Alan immediately knocked it out of Ralph's palm and as he bent down to pick it up Ralph shoved him. He fell down onto the concrete and scraped his knee. Ralph bent down quickly and picked up the money. Alan stayed down in the 'on your marks' position and examined his injured knee which was grazed but not bleeding.

"Now look what you've done."

"It was your fault. You shouldn't have tried to pinch my money."

"I didn't try and pinch it."

"What did you knock it out of my hand for, then?"

"I was only having a bit of fun."

"Funny fun."

Alan stood up and, in silence, they walked down the near-empty Kop to the wall behind the goal. They looked round the ground, then at their programmes in silence, while the Kop gradually filled up behind them. Every few minutes Alan grimaced and looked down at his knee. Ralph looked with him and was finally forced to speak.

"Does it hurt?"

Alan nodded his head.

"Not half."

"Soz, I didn't mean to do that."

Alan made no reply, but continued to inspect his knee.

"My dad says you can come with me anytime. Just us two, he says."

"Does he?"

"It's smart isn't it, getting in for nowt? You've got stacks of money left then, to buy things with."

"I'm saving mine."

"What for?"

"I'm saving up. For Christmas."

"I'm going to get some football kit for Christmas, a full goalkeeper's outfit and a jersey like Jackie Moon's."

"My dad says Jackie Moon's no good now."

"He's great. I think he's great, Jackie Moon."

"My dad says he lets too many soft goals in."

"He still saves some blinders though. He's like a cat when he dives."

"My dad says he's too spectacular."

"I think he's great. He's great, Jackie Moon."

Alan turned round, rested his back on the wall, and looked up into the crowd. Ralph put his chin on his hands and looked out across the pitch. Both boys' heads only just cleared the wall top. Then Alan started waving to someone in the crowd.

"Who you waving to, Alan?"

"My dad, he's up there. He always stands there."

Ralph turned round and briefly scanned the faces rising before him. Alan jumped up and sat on the wall, and continued to smile and wave.

The City came out. Ralph started to cheer and jumped down and turned round to face the pitch. As the City came towards the Kop, their supporters held their scarves above their heads and cheered them. Alan held his scarf up. Ralph waved his programme, then he went quiet for a moment as Jackie Moon reached his goal and bent down in the back of the net to put his cap and gloves down. For a second, as he bent down, he was only a few feet way from Ralph, separated from him only by the track and the net. Then Jackie walked out to the 18- yard line, looked back at his goal to estimate the centre, and, with his studs, scratched a mark across the painted line. He trotted back and the City forwards tested him with shots. Any shots passing into the corners of the goal he made no attempt to save, but he watched them all, and with every one he went through the preliminary motions of a dive. One shot into the bottom corner was travelling straight at Ralph and Alan. They ducked instinctively but the net stopped the ball. They looked back over the wall and laughed.

The referee called the captains together. They tossed up and Ralph watched all three bend over to look at the coin on the turf.

"I wonder what they toss up with, Alan?"

"A penny."

"Somebody told me it was half a crown."

"It's a penny."

"I bet they daren't use half a crown or all the captains would be trying to put it into their pockets."

"How can they? They haven't got any pockets."

The two captains parted and the teams lined up as they were. The City supporters on the Kop cheered. Ralph groaned and turned away for a moment.

"What's the matter?"

"I like the City to play this way first, then I can see Jackie Moon down here in the second half."

"I don't. I like it best when they play this way in the second half. It's more exciting then."

The visiting team immediately attacked and, for the first 10 minutes, maintained their pressure. These tactics, so unusual in an away team, unsettled the City: the whole team was gradually pushed back into defence. Their clearances came straight back at them and their attacks rarely progressed over the half way line. It was only Jackie Moon's daring skill that kept the score level. He was being constantly called upon to dive and punch and catch, while his opposite at the other end was allowed to stroll about his goal area at leisure and watch the game.

Ralph was sweating with excitement. Every time Jackie Moon made a save he copied the movement in miniature and repeatedly turned to Alan to endorse his own opinion of Jackie. The crowd was all for Jackie. If it wasn't for Jackie, they said. Then he conceded a corner. When the centre came over, Jackie strode out of goal, jumped with a bunch of players, and under severe pressure double fisted it hard against the head of his own centre half. The ball cannoned back into the open goal before any of the leaping players had landed and reoriented themselves.

Ralph looked in horrified disbelief at the ball in the net just across the track from him and when Jackie came back to retrieve it he was too choked to offer his commiserations. The visiting players trotted back to the centre, uncertain in their reaction to the goal. Without any of their own men to lavish their emotions on, they expressed their pleasure more in amusement than elation.

The crowd was quiet with disappointment and arguments started on the Kop about Jackie Moon's part in the goal. Some said he should have caught it. Some said he did well to get to it at all. Some said he was unlucky and others said if it wasn't for Jackie the City would be six down, never mind one.

But the goal had upset Jackie. The visitors, realising how ineffectual the opposition was, worked hard to consolidate their position and as the pressure on the City increased, Jackie's performance gradually deteriorated. His handling and judgement off the line became unsure. Although the crowd tolerated his first few mistakes in recognition of his earlier deeds, eventually he was accorded the same treatment as the rest of the side. He became another weak component of an unsafe unit. The defenders were unsure about him and hesitated to pass back. Dissension broke out among them and, all the time, there was the barracking of the crowd, increasing in proportion to the display of the City.

Ralph kept quiet. Every time someone shouted an insult at Jackie Moon, Ralph looked round and singled him out; but he never said anything. Alan was barracking with the rest, echoing the insults of the adults around him, looking round for approbation with a grin on his face.

Just before half-time, a long pass down the centre ran too fast for the centre forward and the City centre half gained possession midway in his own half. He stopped the ball, looked for a man and shaped to kick it with his right foot. He changed his mind, changed feet, but by this time the centre forward was challenging him, so he turned round and started to dribble the ball back towards his own goal. Jackie Moon came off his line and called for the back pass. Instead of passing to him, the centre half kept coming with the centre forward now challenging seriously for possession. Jackie came out of his six yard area calling urgently, but still the centre half came, ushering the ball before him, shielding it from his opponent with his body and arms. The centre forward sprinted. Jackie rushed out, collided with his own man and the ball bounced loose. The centre forward rolled it into the empty net and turned round, arms high. Jackie Moon was on the floor, both hands over his face, the centre half close by, holding his head. The crowd was furious. The referee looked at Jackie, beckoned towards the tunnel and the City trainer, who was already waiting on the touchline, raced across the pitch. When he arrived, the centre half got up and walked away shaking his head. Jackie stayed down, still covering his face.

Alan booed loud and long. Ralph watched intensely as the trainer sat Jackie up and held his head back. Blood was running from his nose. The trainer kept wiping it with his sponge, then shaking the sponge on the grass. By the time he had shaken it, fresh blood had appeared below Jackie's nostrils.

The man next to Alan jumped up, and, with his feet braced against the wall, to hold him up, leaned as far over as he could manage.

"Get him off! Get him off while you've a chance! He's useless!"

Alan made a megaphone with his hands:

"Get him off!"

The trainer kept Jackie's head back although the blood had now stopped flowing. He still had his eyes closed but as the trainer helped him to his feet, he opened them and shook his head. The blood started to flow again.

Alan placed his hands to his mouth again.

"Substitute!"

The man next to him agreed.

"Take him off! Anybody'd be better than him."

Alan laughed and Ralph turned on him, almost crying with anger.

"They haven't got anybody better than him."

"They haven't got anybody worse, you mean."

"It wasn't his fault, that goal."

"'Course it was."

"He was waiting for a back pass."

"Waiting for a busted nose you mean, 'cos that's all he got."

"It wasn't his fault."

"He deserved it as well."

The trainer was talking urgently to Jackie as he sponged his face. Jackie kept nodding. He walked slowly back to his goal, wiping his forehead with his sleeve.

"He's not hurt. He's putting it on because he let a soft goal in."

"How do you know? He got Whittaker's head straight in his face."

"He's just putting it on."

"You can't talk."

Alan turned and looked at him.

"What do you mean?"

"What about that bit of a scratch on your leg? You nearly cried over that."

"Did I heck!"

"Not half."

"It hurt."

"Hurt! It didn't even bleed. If you'd have had a busted nose they'd be carrying you away in a coffin now."

At half-time Ralph went for a hot dog. When he returned Alan was not there. He did not return until the teams were coming back on the field. Ralph moved up to make a space at the wall for him. Alan stayed on the step above.

"I'm going to stand up there with my dad, Ralph."

Ralph turned right round and looked up at him.

"That's dirty."

"Why is it? You can come if you want."

"What do you want to go and stand with your dad for?"

"'Cos I do."

"That's not right, Alan, when you came with me."

"I can please myself, can't I?"

"When I got you in free as well."

The visiting goalkeeper moved towards them, talking to his right back, emphasising his account with flamboyant gestures of his hands. The full back stopped and the goalkeeper left him and continued to walk towards the goal. Alan waited for him to take up his position, then he half turned and glanced up the Kop.

"I'm off then. Coming?"

"You're not coming with me again if you do."

"I'm not bothered. You're not coming to play in our house again either."

"If I'd wanted, I could have gone up in the stand with

my dad. When they've finished, all the turnstile men can go up in the centre stand if they like."

"Can they heck."

They both looked across the pitch and up at the main stand. Behind the front few rows the faces disappeared in darkness, and along the full length of the stand the darkness was being continually picked by the flaring of matches lighting cigarettes.

"They can. They have a special row reserved for turnstile men, at the back, and they can take anybody there who they like."

"Why don't you go then."

"I'm going to. I'm going to find my dad and go with him."

"Go on then."

The referee started the second half and the swell of noise from the crowd drew their attention back to the game. The ball immediately went out of play for a throw-in. Alan turned round and started to push his way up through the crowd. Ralph followed him, pushed past him and disappeared up the Kop. He reached the top of the Kop and continued down the wide steps to the big blue gate and the row of turnstiles at the bottom. The gate and all the turnstiles were locked. Ralph ran round to the other end of the ground and worked his way down to the wall in time to see Jackie Moon run out and dispossess the inside right by diving at his feet.

My First Dog

Bought from a farm
He brought the yard smells home with him.
A sheepdog
Bred for work
He stalked the children's rabbit on the lawn.
Unimpressed and ignorant of the rules
It stood its ground and nibbled dandelion.

He must have seen a cat
Or smelled the bitch across the road
In heat.
The driver never stopped
And when I picked him up
Already dead, his eyes were glazing over
With thin ice.

I had to dig a proper grave,
Three feet
Squared off
With sides.
Not like the pulled up sods
And shallow scoops for minor pets
Like guinea pigs and budgerigars.

With Moss, 1980s.

A shocking job
Like burying a child.
It made me cry
The first time since my father died.
Never again, I said,
But pain subsides.
Next spring I bought another one.
I said the same when that one died.

Northern Voices

Barry was a guest of Hull Literary Club in the early 1970s, along with fellow writers Leonard Barras and Mike Haywood. He has saved the introductory speech although he cannot remember who wrote it.

Barry Hines was born in 1939 at Hoyland Common, a mining village near Barnsley, where he still lives. His father was a miner. Barry's academic record at grammar school was poor, his sporting record brilliant and he played soccer for the England Grammar Schools' 11 — 'Got to get that in, more important than the Nobel prize, that,' to use his own words. Continuing in his own words: 'Had a spell as an apprentice mining surveyor, and various labouring jobs, before entering Loughborough College to study Physical Education. Then taught in London for two years. Came back north in 1963, then started writing seriously. Married, two children. Still teaching in local comprehensive school. I think there's enough there.'

These are the clues to the qualities of Barry Hines, as a person and as a writer. There is a natural modesty amounting to reticence, a tendency to understate, rather than exaggerate, his own importance and a real sense that writing — however serious a matter it is to him — is perhaps of less value to the community than teaching, a job I know he loves.

Not unexpectedly, much of his work is concerned with physical activity rather than mental anguish and his early poems like, *You Can't Beat a Cig Packet* crystallises this concern with characteristic economy, precision and knowledge.

Like Leonard Barras*, Barry Hines is a brilliant miniaturist, but he made the death-defying leap — a phrase I am sure he would approve of — into the larger scale work of plays and novels early in his career. His first novel *The Blinder* was published in 1966 and is about the dilemma of a young man, still at school, who is gifted both academically and as a soccer player, and is consequently torn between University and the local football club. The title derives from the well known phrase — well known to me anyway — 'playing a blinder.'

Obviously the story is a projection of Barry Hines' own youthful conflict of interests, though to what extent it is autobiographical is hardly for me to say; I have no evidence that he went to bed with the wife of the chairman of his local soccer club, as does the hero of the book, though I would tend to think not. What is self-evident, to me anyway — a lifelong and passionate soccer fan — is the ringing truth of those sequences concerned with the game, both on the field and in the dressing room. The

---

* Barras was a Wallsend-born writer who worked in the shipyards of the north-east while writing plays for the radio and stage, mainly set in working-class communities of the 1930s.

dialogue between players is terse, colourful, and authentic, but goes beyond documentary reportage, which can be done with a tape-recorder, to give a deeper insight into character, relationship and the reality of the professional so-called sporting life.

My feeling is that the football scenes work better than the others; off the field the characters tend to behave too much like people in novels—in detail the small change of language and behaviour is neat and sharp but at times the plot controls the characters, instead of the reverse. Nevertheless, out of this colourful and lively beginning was to grow the next book *A Kestrel for a Knave* which was later to be transposed into the film *Kes* and even gave the name Kestrel Productions to the bright young film company who had the wit, perception and bloody-minded determination to make and show the film in the teeth of a brutally insensitive film industry.

The theme of the novel is simple enough: a study of a working-class kid in Barnsley, none too bright, crawling unwillingly to his secondary modern school once a day, counting each day as a step nearer the dead-end job like his father's before him. Then the boy captures a bird—a wild kestrel—trains it patiently and with love—love for the process and the relationship, not for the bird, for this is not a schmaltzy Disney-like relationship. Indeed, the boy's admiration is for the bird's independence, not for its affection, because it betrays none.

The relationship ends, harshly and brutally, and life goes on. But in the process Hines, through his simple

Daivd Bradley as
Billy Casper in *Kes*.

story, draws a massive cross-section through our society, the way we educate our children and what we do with them once they have been through the motions of education. It is a story about an underdog and how the underdog has his day and how that day ends. In the boy's relationship with the bird is the poetry that every man is capable of—the kind of poetic feeling that is enshrined in many apparently mundane activities; the training of pigeons and whippets, the patient cultivation of plants and flowers on waste ground allotments, even the relationship between men and their work.

Hines is aware of the work factor in men's lives—ennobling and a brutalising experience. He is aware of the deep humanity and the subdued violence in the lives of his people. He is no romantic and there is little room in his work for sentimentalising over the dignity of labour; but even as the people live out their narrow, grey and sometimes violent existence, he is quick to perceive the native wit and humanity, and eager to point out that he is on their side.

Locked Out

I saw a child outside a butcher's shop
Knocking on the door for his mother.
I could see his mother through the window,
Talking with some others,
Deafened by the butcher sawing bone.
He looked so tiny by that massive door,
Too small to reach the knob,
So he knocked louder
Shouting through the wood,
His cries unheard,
Until the butcher turned to serve.

When they heard him shouting there
They all began to laugh,
Which silenced him,
Then frightened him,
Then made him cry with fear.

It's a terrible thing to be locked out.
Especially when your pleas are heard,
And answered
By nothing more than laughter
From the other side.

When We Were Heroes

Richard Benson, *The Observer*.
Sunday December 4, 2005

"Oh yes, I remember going to see Kes," said my cousin,
Gary Hollingworth, 49, ex-miner turned social worker
and South Yorkshire raconteur. "I went to see it when it
first came out; we all did. I went with a mate, and both of
us were interested in history, and I remember when we
came out he said, "That was our history, that film". And
it was—not the Marquess of wherever for once, but our
history. And looking back, I think it belonged to that
time in the 1970s when there was that working-class
confidence; wages were going up, so you were getting
better off, and we felt as if we had power in our hands. It
was reflected in what we wore; there was the skinhead
thing and then glam rock, people wearing platforms and
glitter, blokes at the pit with feather cuts, using after-
shave and deodorant in the baths and their dads pillock-
ing them for it... it was part of a unique time."

In South Yorkshire, mention of *Kes* often elicits anec-
dotes such as Gary's. It is a bit like mentions of the
Beatles in Liverpool, a reminder of how art can give
people a sense of representation. Filmed around Barnsley

using many locals as actors, Ken Loach's 1969 film adaptation of Barry Hines's novel, *A Kestrel for a Knave*, is woven into people's lives. Gary worked at Grimethorpe colliery with Freddie Fletcher, who played Jud Casper; as a schoolgirl, Gary's wife, Heather, was taught by Colin Welland, who played Mr Farthing the English teacher.

Everyone you meet seems to have known or been one of the actors or extras, and it is an enduring point of pride that when the film was shown in the US, it had to be subtitled because of the accents. Both my mother and father's families had lived in South Yorkshire for generations, and after we moved to the East Riding, they used to watch the film with the sort of romantic longing associated with Ireland or pre-war eastern Europe, despite the fact that the locations lay only 45 minutes' drive down the M62.

Pomona Books, a new Yorkshire-based publishing company inspired by the working-class British fiction of the 1960s and 1970s, and operating on principles similar to those of Manchester's Factory Records, has just reissued two other Barry Hines novels, as part of an ongoing campaign to get him the recognition that Pomona founder Mark Hodkinson believes he deserves. Both books are set in South Yorkshire. *The Price of Coal* was first published in 1979, and tells the story of a royal visit and an underground accident at a colliery. *Looks and Smiles* from 1981 is a love story set in recessionary Sheffield where unemployment is breaking up old communities and ways of living. As a pair, they foreshadowed changes that would affect the area in the coming decades. Between 1981 and 2004, 67,000 jobs would be lost in mining and similar numbers in the steel and manufacturing industries.

The losses, coupled with what now seems like astonishing neglect on the part of the last Conservative government, had severe and well-documented effects on the region, although, in recent years, EU funding has brought new jobs and new regeneration-scheme landscapes. Spoil heaps are now grassed over and planted with trees; vast, gleaming white call-centre complexes and retail parks stand where collieries and coking plants used to be; there are new red-and-beige housing developments and smooth new roads and brightly coloured distribution warehouses owned by globo-corps like IKEA.

A village near Barnsley has its own reality TV show (*Priest Idol*). South Yorkshire Police has just become the first force in Britain to do podcasts. And there are new people; Doncaster has attracted communities from Africa and the Middle East which, according to mayor Martin Winter, have been well-received because of the town's history of welcoming outsiders who came to work in the mining industry. All this exists side by side with traditional terraces, shops, farms and 19th-century brick churches and pubs. There is, in some places, a sense of traditional and future Britain rubbing shoulders.

What does the man who conceived *Kes*, and *The Price of Coal*, make of his world 40 years after he began writing about it? On a crisp, clear autumn afternoon, I drove with him from his home in Sheffield to Hoyland Common, the old mining village where he grew up, to find out.

Hines was born in 1939, in a two-up, two-down semi-detached house on the lane leading out of the village towards the pit. The eldest of two sons born of a miner and a miner's daughter, he spent a happy childhood playing in the woods, keeping baby magpies and watching the hawks preying on the hedgerows and verges. He left grammar school at 15 without doing his exams and, out of 'a sort of bravado' towards the other boys who thought him a cissie, he went down the pit as an apprentice mining surveyor.

This proved to be something of an awakening. On the first day, he was terrified as the cage took him underground and, once there, he sensed the scorn of the miners, who thought surveyors didn't do real work. One day, he was crawling on his hands and knees along a low passage near the coal face when he saw Bill Hawksworth, a neighbour from Hoyland Common, cutting coal. Barry felt pleased to see him and said hello, but as Bill recognised Barry, he failed to smile. In fact, he looked disgusted. 'Is this the best job you could get?' he said, and resumed work.

Barry went back to school, trained as a teacher and eventually moved back to Hoyland Common, writing novels in the school library when the children had gone home.

The village looks smarter now and his childhood home

much 'posher' than it did when he lived there (to the bemusement of some locals, done-up miners' cottages in some villages have now become highly desirable properties). But there are other changes he notices as we walk down the alley beside his old home and look out over the backyards and gardens. These used to be communal, but are now all partitioned up. In the streets beyond, there are few people walking, whereas in the pre-big-supermarket-shop era it would have been full of people running errands for bits at the shops.

"I suppose everyone is in their houses, if they're not at work," he says, his rich and warm Barnsleyish accent lightly tempered by teacherly tones. "To me, the difference now is that it's as if people live in their house, like a bubble, watching television maybe, then get into their car, and then go to the supermarket, all that without talking to anyone. Maybe that's not bad, but if people are out a lot, it means you know each other and you feel safe, and you feel part of something, part of the village. I think it is important, but you know things change. People change. I'll tell you what, though [he points towards the border of a garden on his old street], I don't like that bloody leylandii hedge. They're horrible. Cutting people off from each other again!"

We walk over to a playing field opposite ('King George's field they call it; we used to take the piss out of the name — how come King George had that particular field?') and because it reminds me a bit of the football match in *Kes*, I ask him about the lasting impact of the book and the film. He is happy enough to talk about *Kes*, but struck by how long ago it all seems. There is no secret to its success, he says; it was because it 'was about things they could see around them. For a lot of children, it will have been the first and last book they were ever given to read. If that was what they saw around them, they would be interested to read about those things.' People have never said all that much to him about it, he claims, but then 'people in Hoyland Common don't make a fuss and palaver about things'.

He is, perhaps, too modest. You can tell the film has a wider and enduring appeal by the way it is reinterpreted by new generations. According to Dan Johnson, a geography student from Barnsley (his cub scout leader played the librarian), the film had a different meaning for people of his age. To many in the 1970s, it seemed like an exposé of the state education system, but to him it now seems more a way of 'preserving the unique character of the pit villages'.

It wasn't only the pit closures that were eroding that character, Dan said, but also the consumer monoculture that came with the new industries, all that screen-watching and anonymous buildings that turned a place from, as he put it, 'a somewhere to an anywhere'. As he said, ex-miners will soon put you straight if you get lyrical about pit work, but still … there was something about *Kes* that made you think about what might get lost.

I found myself thinking about this as Barry chatted to an old neighbour he met on the street ('I'm a comer-in to Hoyland,' I overheard her say. 'I've been here 62 years, but still ...'). I remembered the visits to Highgate, my family's home village, which seemed like visits to a place where everyone seemed somehow powered by bigger batteries than people in other places. Most of the men in my mother's family worked or had worked as miners and they had a wisecracking, intimate cama-raderie that I suppose came from the mutual dependency born of risking your lives together underground every day. They were friendlier, closer to each other and yet more welcoming to outsiders, which is a very unusual combination.

I always felt proud of my grandad, an ex-miner who played the drums, and sang, and did cabaret in working-men's clubs, and sometimes used to play us the best tracks of his brass band records when we went to see him. I don't want to sound like an old-world we-made-our-own-entertainment-type, but, to me, his music, and the bands and the clubs and institutes, and my cousins' intri-cate union badges were like *Kes* in a way — people creat-ing their own culture. Stuff like that tends to come into view at precisely the moment it begins to disappear; can you retain the positive bits without turning the world into a museum?

I remembered a conversation I had with another cousin, Alan Hollingworth, Gary's brother, who still works underground at Rossington Colliery (one of South Yorkshire's two remaining working pits, due to be moth-balled next February), and his wife, Pat. 'People move on more now,' he said. 'Men come to the pit and stay two years and then move on, go and do something else. Since the strike, people have come to see it as just a job, something to give you a wage that lets you do what you want to do.'

Would people turn the clock back if they could? I asked. He and Pat both thought for a minute. No, probably not, she said. Not now the area is 'coming nice'. 'You've to be careful you don't look back with rose-tinted glasses, you know,' she says. 'There was definitely less crime because we all knew each other, but then again there was everyone knowing all your business. We appreciated what we had more then, but we're more prosperous now. We've got more material things, it's just that there seems to be less ... communication, somehow.'

This modern, call-centre-world anomie is not unique to South Yorkshire. In fact people's warm openness remains striking, as architect Will Alsop, helping to redevelop Barnsley on the model of a Tuscan hill village, recently pointed out. It is just that because the communities here have been so close, self-reliant and independent in spirit, and because the economic transition has been so dramatic, it throws up some interesting insights into life in Britain in the 21st century.

I remembered another conversation, this time with Gary. He had worked in mines for 17 years, most of them as a ventilation officer. He told the people running schemes to get ex-miners back into work that he wanted to retrain as a teacher. He had always been interested in helping people, he said, thought he could study if he got the chance. They couldn't help him, they said. Wouldn't he like to think about plumbing or joinery instead?

Eventually, Gary got work at a residential children's home, and then funded himself through diplomas in social work and higher education at Hull University to end up as a senior social worker. Soon, he was promoted to team leader. The work became incessant. He began to feel run-down and kept getting eye and throat infections. His doctor diagnosed — and this in a man who had witnessed many explosions and injuries hundreds of feet underground — stress.

"I thought, stress? What do you think I am, a ... poof? That was the inverted snob still in me, but he was right. I think part of the cause of that is because when you worked at the pit, your weekends were relaxing, having a drink, not rushing off to bloody garden centres or doing DIY. We've all had those values pushed on us somehow. I've been making a conscious effort to get back to that old way lately. To learn how to do nothing on Sunday afternoons again."

The bottom of Barry' street used to peter out into a lane across fields that led to the pit. In the old days, you would hear the men coming back from a shift before you saw them, their boots clattering on the road. At the end of the nightshift, the men would march straight up, past Barry' house, to the pub where the landlord would be waiting with hundreds of half-filled pint glasses, ready to top them up for the men as they came in.

I tell Hines that, reading *Looks and Smiles* when it came out, Gary had been struck by Hines's description of the then new companies as appearing less solid, less committed to the social structure than the old steelworks and pits. ('The factories that had been built looked temporary and insubstantial, as if they could be removed overnight,' Hines wrote. 'Even their names seemed impermanent: Styro, Eno Fabrication, PI Products.' *Looks and Smiles* seemed to evoke nostalgia for old industrial communities even as *The Price of Coal* clearly rues the associated hardships. Did Barry think that mining, which he thought 'the hardest job in the world', gave the men who did it something special that people did not get from the new kinds of work?

"There is a sense of pride," he says. "It's a dangerous job and it is hard work. And there's pride in being able to do that, isn't there? And they were good at it. They were very good at it."

In the breaker's yard which now stands at the end of the street, a man in overalls walks out of an office and watches us. The evening lights are coming on in Hoyland Common, and the distant noise from cars on the main street is increasing as five o'clock approaches. I don't know if it's something to do with the moment, or if it's just because Barry Hines seems such a kind man, but my penultimate question comes out as a bit of a blurt. The thing is, I say, for my generation, industries that actually make things have always seemed to be on the way out, and the industries we're supposed to be excited about seem mostly to involve moving paper about and they're boring. Most people I know hate their work as much as anyone ever did, but they don't have the sense of embattled piss-taking and comradeship that you find in *The Price of Coal*. So, to be honest, I can't help romanticising a world where people actually made things, even though the work was hard. And I'm not the only one. Even some younger people now feel a sort of nostalgia for times they didn't even live through themselves. Do you think that's silly?

"No, it's not silly," he says. "The people who made those things and designed them were proud of them. I mean, most of the blokes in Sheffield who worked in the steel factories were proud. You would be, if you were walking down the street in Brighton or somewhere and you saw 'Made in Sheffield'. You'd say, "Look at that! I made that" or, "So and so made that". Or, "We did that"."

Has anything come to replace that?

"I've thought a lot about that," says Hines, as we turn and head back up the street to where the car is parked, "but I don't know. I just don't know ... maybe the time will come when no one will bother about that, when no one will remember that feeling, when it won't matter. Maybe it's come now."

Early 1960s.

Starlings

Something repels me in starlings,
It's their panic-stricken gluttony,
And evil greens and purples,
Like bluebottles;
But most of all
It's their cocky ugliness,
That sleek and rakish look,
Like men with patent leather hair.

I look for the bibbed robin
With its baby charm
And mouse-ish fur.
Or the blue tit,
That glob of twinkling iridescence.
Even the dull sparrow is welcome,
Reliable like a working man.
They're all welcome at my table;
Except starlings.

I know all life is sacred
And I wouldn't see it starve.
But a few seconds of its presence
Angers me.
I have to knock
And make it fly away.
Am I wrong in this?
Should ugliness be allowed an equal share?
Or am I right
To repel it,
And prefer beauty in its place?

Christmas Afternoon

He lay on his belly and pulled the bolt of his bagatelle. The silver ball shot up the tunnel and bounced round the shiny pins. He pushed a chocolate into his mouth and stood up before the ball had stopped. His face was flushed with the fire and he looked sick with sweets. His presents were strewn around the rug, already discarded. His mother and dad were asleep in the armchairs, sprawled out like stuffed Guy Fawkes. The television was on but the sound had been turned down, and a circus audience were miming laughter.

He picked up his new air rifle and stood by the window. The yard was deserted. Snow had begun to fall from the leaden sky, the flakes gathering in the ridges of the bony earth. A robin was searching for food under the window. He stood still behind the curtains and watched it poke about among the stones.

He picked a mince pie off a plate on the sideboard and opened the door. The robin flew to the wall at the bottom of the yard, and watched him crumble the pastry and scatter it down. He went inside and closed the door. The slug fitted neatly into the barrel, and the gun straightened with an oily click. He inched the window open, poked the barrel through, and knelt down to wait.

The robin hopped along the wall top, from side to side, as though the bricks were hot. Then it came, straight down and started peck-pecking at the food, quickly, nervously, twitching its wings across its back.

The boy lined it up through the sights, the knob between the V against the rusty red background. Splat! His mother jumped, and her eyelids shot open. She looked round then flopped back again. The boy opened the door and went outside. The robin was lying on its side among the crumbs and currants. He picked it up and it was still warm through the feathers. There was no mark to show where the slug had entered. He lifted the dustbin lid and dropped it with the ashes, then went back inside. He lay down on the rug and pulled the bolt of the bagatelle, feeling behind him for chocolate with his other hand.

* Published originally in *Northern Drift* (Blackie and Son Ltd, 1980).

'You don't like "kes"? But everybody likes "kes".'

Full circle: Barry as a baby and nearly 70 years later, retired back to Hoyland Common.

POMONA BOOKS

Pomona is a wholly independent publisher dedicated to bringing before the public the work of prodigiously talented writers. Our books can be purchased on-line at:

www.pomonauk.com

Pomona backlist